Contents

Answers to Revision Questions are online:
www.hodderplus.co.uk/cceagcsescience

Introduction

The purpose of this revision guide is to help students who are taking GCSE Chemistry or the Chemistry component of Double Award Science fulfill their potential in the course. The book outlines key chemistry facts and explains the underlying concepts in an approachable style. Particular attention is paid to topics and types of questions that have traditionally caused most difficulty.

As well as helping with knowledge and understanding, the book will give useful guidance in examination techniques in the form of Exam tips. Many of the tips highlight common misconceptions and mistakes made by students during examinations. They also explain how to use the correct terms and critical words to maximise the student's marks.

Using a carefully planned revision strategy which incorporates the reinforcement of core knowledge and essential understanding, this book will assist you to achieve your very best, whether you are striving to obtain an A or A* grade, or hoping to achieve a Grade C. This book is intended to complement its companion text, *GCSE Chemistry for CCEA (Second Edition)*. The sixteen chapters are arranged in two units. Content in unit 1 will be examined in unit 1 tests and content in unit 2 in unit 2 tests. However some sections are required for both but this is made clear in the individual chapters. In each chapter the most important points in each topic are explained and understanding is built up through the use of questions and typical answers. At the end of each chapter there are revision questions (without answers) which can be used for testing knowledge and understanding. The answers to these questions and the *Data Leaflet* can be found on the website www.hodderplus.co.uk/cceagcsescience

Advice on preparing for examinations

The most important piece of advice is **prepare, prepare, prepare.** But how do you prepare? There is a document issued by CCEA for your benefit. It is called the **subject specification** and it gives detailed information about what you must know, understand and be able to do. The examiners are bound by it! No examiner is permitted to set any question that lies outside the specification. To obtain a free copy, visit the website www.ccea.org.uk and follow the links to qualifications, specifications. The same website gives you access to the **latest GCSE past papers**, **mark schemes** and **Chief Examiner Reports** which provide information for teachers and candidates on candidate performance in each series of examinations.

To help you navigate this revision book some material is in a coloured background. The arrangement is this:

All material not on a tinted background is required for foundation tier students following either the GCSE Double Award Science or the GCSE Chemistry specifications. **ALL FOUNDATION TIER MATERIAL CAN ALSO BE ASSESSED AT HIGHER TIER.**

Material required for the higher tier students following either the GCSE Double Award Science or the GCSE Chemistry specification is identified with a green tinted background.

Material required for foundation tier students following the GCSE Chemistry specification is identified with a blue tinted background. **ALL FOUNDATION TIER MATERIAL CAN BE ASSESSED AT HIGHER TIER.**

Material required for higher tier students following the GCSE Chemistry specification is identified with a red tinted background.

But remember, if you are in the slightest doubt about what you must know – look at the specification.

Begin your revision early and make certain there is nothing in the specification that you do not understand. If there is, then ask your teacher. Examiners have a strange knack of asking the questions on topics you didn't get round to revising!

Many pupils fail to maximise their performance because they misread the questions. Remember that examiners can only mark what they see in the paper in front of them, not what they think you meant to write! So read each question carefully and do exactly what you are asked to do.

Assessment objectives (AOs) summarise the knowledge and skills candidates are expected to develop as they follow a GCSE course. The three different assessment objectives are listed in the following table.

AO1	Recall, select and communicate their knowledge and understanding of Chemistry
AO2	Apply skills, knowledge and understanding of Chemistry in practical and other contexts
AO3	Analyse and evaluate evidence, make reasoned judgements and draw conclusions based on evidence

AO1 questions – these test your **knowledge and understanding** of the chemistry content in the specification.

AO2 questions – these involve the **application of skills**. These skills include the **drawing of graphs, writing formulae or equations, carrying out calculations** and **applying your knowledge in unfamiliar situations**.

AO3 questions will often involve the presentation of results from an experiment, or a set of data and asking you to **analyse and evaluate the evidence and make considered judgements** on the evidence provided. AO3 is tested in your unit tests and in the Controlled Assessment Task.

Every chemistry examination paper, other than the controlled assessment task must test each of AO1, AO2 and AO3. To develop good examination technique in answering AO2 and AO3 questions in particular, it is important that you reinforce your knowledge and skills by practising on examination questions. Examples can be found in this book, in the companion text *GCSE Chemistry for CCEA (Second Edition)*, or in past examination papers.

QWC questions

There will be Quality of Written communication (QWC) questions **worth 6 marks**. While these questions will be testing your ability to communicate Chemistry information in a logical way using appropriate scientific terminology, you can only access the full range of marks available if you understand and describe the Chemistry involved.

If you are concerned about the mathematical skills you need, look at section 3.4 (GCSE Chemistry) or section 3.8 (Double Award Science) in the relevant specification and practise these skills by doing the mathematical examples in this book!

If all this seems a little daunting take heart! **The vast majority of GCSE DAS and Chemistry students are successful** and you are likely to be so too. You have a revision book specially written for the CCEA examinations. It will help you achieve the highest grade of which you are capable. It is now up to you to use it.

1 Elements, Compounds and Mixtures

The Periodic Table lists all known elements.

- An **element** is a substance that consists of only one type of atom – an element cannot be broken down into simpler substances by chemical means.
- A **compound** is a substance that consists of two or more different elements chemically combined.
- An **atom** is the simplest particle of an element that can exist on its own in a stable environment.
- A **molecule** is a particle that consists of two or more atoms chemically bonded together.

Seven elements are diatomic. 'Diatomic' means that these elements exist as molecules containing two identical atoms covalently bonded. The seven elements are hydrogen, nitrogen, oxygen, fluorine, chlorine, bromine and iodine.

Exam tip

The definitions of an element, an atom, a compound and a molecule are common questions.

Particle diagrams Revised

Diagrams using differently shaded and different sized circles to represent atoms of different elements are often used in chemistry.

- The diagram may represent a pure substance, which may be an element or a compound.
- The diagram may represent a mixture, which may be made up of elements, of compounds, or of elements and compounds.
- Diatomic elements are easily recognised in these diagrams because the two atoms in the molecules are the same.

There is only one type of particle (a **pure substance**) which contains two different atoms chemically bonded together – so this a **compound**

There are two types of particle so this is a **mixture**): one is an atom of an element and one is a molecule of compound (different atoms). This is a mixture of **one element** and **one compound**

- If the particles are spaced well apart, the diagram represents a gas.
- If the particles are very close together but not in a regular arrangement, the diagram represents a liquid.
- If the particles are very close together and in a regular arrangement, the diagram represents a solid.

Most elements are described as either metal or non-metal.

Note: *Silicon and germanium are described as semi-metals.*

Metals and non-metals differ in their physical properties and you need to be able to classify a substance as metallic or non-metallic based on given physical properties. The terms below are the commonly used physical properties:

- *Thermal conductivity* is the ability to conduct heat – for example, copper is a good thermal conductor.
- *Electrical conductivity* is the ability to conduct electricity – for example, silver is a very good electrical conductor; polythene does not conduct electricity.
- *Ductility* is the ability to be drawn out into wires – for example, copper is ductile.
- *Malleability* is the ability to be hammered into shape (without breaking) – for example, iron is malleable.
- *Melting point* is the temperature at which a solid changes into a liquid on heating – for example, iron has a high melting point; chlorine has a low melting point.
- *Sonority* is the ability to ring when struck – for example, brass is sonorous.

The table below gives some of the physical properties of metals and non-metals.

Physical properties of elements

Physical property	Metals	Non-metals
Thermal conductivity	High	Poor
Electrical conductivity	High	Poor (except graphite)
Ductility	Ductile	Not ductile
Malleability	Malleable	Not malleable
Melting point	High (Group 1 metals have low melting points)	Low (except diamond and graphite)
Sonority	Sonorous	Not sonorous

Exam tip

Watch out for graphite and diamond because they are the only non-metals you study that have very high melting points and solid graphite conducts electricity. Their other properties are those of non-metals. Remember that most non-metals are gases, liquids or low-melting point solids.

Exam tip

A typical question will give information about an unknown substance – for example, good electrical conductor, melting point of 660 °C, ductile and malleable. These properties indicate that the substance is a metal.

Mixtures

Revised

- A mixture is defined as two or more substances mixed together, which are usually easy to separate.
- Solids that dissolve in water are described as **soluble**; solids that do not dissolve in water are described as **insoluble**.
- A solid that dissolves is called a **solute**; the liquid in which the solute dissolves (usually water) is called the **solvent**.
- The resulting mixture of a solute dissolved in a solvent is called a **solution**.
- Liquids that mix (for example alcohol and water) are described as **miscible**; liquids that do not mix (for example oil and water) are described as **immiscible**.

- The method of separating a mixture depends on the properties of the substances in the mixture.

The following is a list of **separation techniques** that may be used.

Separation techniques

Filtration separates an insoluble solid from a liquid.

- Filtration can be used to separate a mixture of a soluble solid and an insoluble solid once added to a solvent. The filtered solution is called the **filtrate** and the solid remaining in the filter paper is called the **residue**.
- This method can be used to separate sand mixed with water – the sand would be the residue and the filtrate would be water.
- This method can also be used to separate sand from salt. Add water to the mixture of salt and sand and then heat and stir to make sure all the salt dissolves. Filter to remove the sand from the mixture. The residue is the sand and the filtrate is the salt solution.

Recrystallisation separates a solute from a solution (the solution is usually the filtrate from filtration).

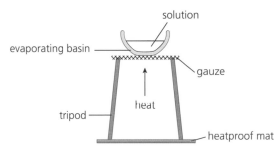
↑ **Recrystallisation**

- The solution is heated gently in an evaporating basin – the water boils off, leaving the solid solute behind in the evaporating basin.
- This method can be used to obtain salt from a salt solution, or simply to see if there are any dissolved solids in a liquid sample.

A **separating funnel** can be used to separate immiscible liquids – for example oil and water – based on a difference in their densities (the less dense liquid is the top layer).

- The mixture of liquids is placed in a separating funnel. The separating funnel is clamped and the liquids separate into two layers. The stopper should then be removed from the top of the flask.
- The bottom layer (water in the diagram) is run into a beaker below by opening the tap. When the junction between the layers reaches the tap, the tap is closed. The top layer can be then run out into another beaker.
- Water is a relatively dense liquid and is often the bottom layer but not always. The more dense liquid is the bottom layer.

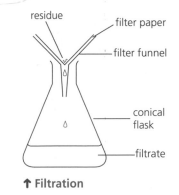
↑ **Filtration**

Exam tip

It is important that you can draw a fully labelled diagram of the assembled apparatus used to separate mixtures. These questions can be asked in different units throughout the specification.

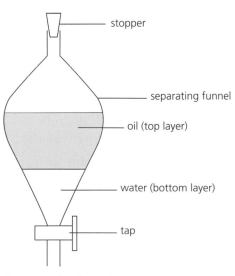
↑ **Separating funnel**

Simple distillation separates a solvent from a solution (e.g. water from salt solution) or one of two miscible liquids (e.g. a mixture of ethanol and water).

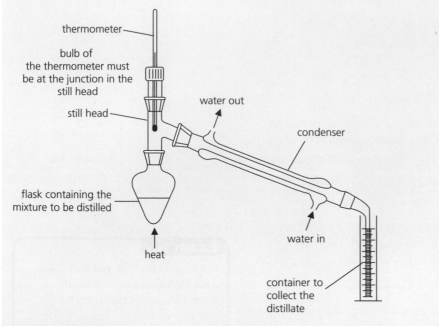

↑ **Simple distillation**

- If a liquid in the mixture is flammable (e.g. ethanol) then a water bath is used to heat the flask rather than a Bunsen burner.

- Distillation separates substances because they have **different boiling points**. The temperature shown by the thermometer will remain the same while a particular liquid is boiling off.

- For salt solution, the solvent (water – boiling point 100 °C) will boil off and collect as the distillate, and the thermometer will remain at 100 °C until all the water is boiled off. The salt will remain in the flask.

- For a mixture of ethanol (boiling point 79 °C) and water (boiling point 100 °C), the ethanol will boil off first and the temperature will remain at 79 °C until all the ethanol has boiled off.

- Even at exactly 79 °C, some water will evaporate and the ethanol collected will not be pure. Fractional distillation is a better method of separating liquids when the boiling points are reasonably close together.

- A condenser is a glass cylinder with another cylinder around it. Gases pass though the middle tube and cold water runs between the cylinders providing a cold surface for the gases to condense on.

- The cooling water must go in at the bottom of the condenser and out at the top to ensure that the condenser is filled with water at all times.

- Anti-bumping granules are added to the contents of the flask to promote smooth boiling.

Fractional distillation separates miscible liquids, such as ethanol and water, or crude oil or the components of liquid air using **differences in their boiling points**.

> **Exam tip**
> The liquid which is collected in distillation is called the distillate.

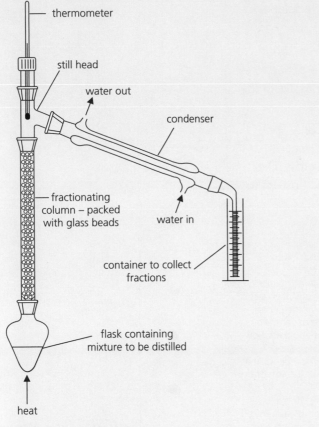

- thermometer
- still head
- water out
- condenser
- fractionating column – packed with glass beads
- water in
- container to collect fractions
- flask containing mixture to be distilled
- heat

↑ **Fractional distillation**

- Fractional distillation uses the same apparatus as simple distillation with a fractionating column on top of the flask.
- This method provides better separation of miscible liquids than simple distillation because evaporated liquids below their boiling point do not reach the condenser – they condense on the glass beads in the fractionating column and return to the flask.
- The container collecting the distillate can be changed to collect distillates at different temperatures – distillates collected at different temperatures are called **fractions**.
- If a mixture of ethanol and water is fractionally distilled, a fraction would be collected around 79 °C, which would be purer ethanol than the ethanol obtained by simple distillation.
- Fractional distillation should be used to separate miscible liquids that have boiling points which are close together.

Exam tip

You will not be expected to draw the apparatus for simple or fractional distillation but just recognise them, label various pieces of apparatus or the distillate and answer questions on how it separates mixtures.

Magnetism separates a magnetic substance from a non-magnetic substance – for example, a mixture of iron (magnetic) and sulfur (non-magnetic).

If a magnet is put close to a mixture of iron and sulfur, the iron is attracted to the magnet and the sulfur is not. If a mixture of iron and sulfur is heated, it reacts to form iron(II) sulfide, which is non-magnetic. This is often used to show that a chemical reaction makes a new substance.

Chromatography separates the components of a mixture in a solution using **differences in their solubility in a solvent**.

Paper chromatography is commonly used. A pencil line is drawn about 1 cm from the bottom of a piece of chromatography paper. A pencil cross is drawn on the pencil line. Pencil is used because it will not dissolve in the solvent.

The mixture to be investigated is dissolved in a small volume of a solvent – water, ethanol or another solvent or a mixture of solvents. A capillary tube is used to spot a sample of the solution on the cross. The paper is then placed in a container with enough solvent in the bottom to reach the bottom of the paper.

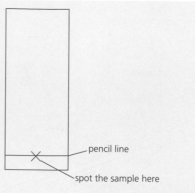

↑ **Setting up paper chromatography**

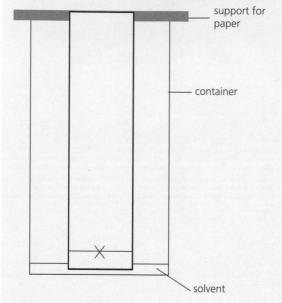

↑ **Chromatography**

- Allow the solvent to be drawn up the chromatography paper.
- When the solvent is close to the top of the paper, remove the paper from the solvent and mark how far the solvent has travelled with a pencil line. This is called the **solvent front.**
- The mixture should have separated into different components, which are seen as spots on the paper.

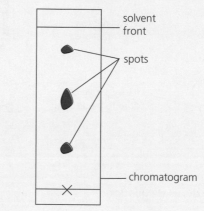

- The spot that travel furthest on the chromatography paper is the component that is most soluble in the solvent.

- If a spot does not move up the chromatography paper during chromatography, it is not soluble in the solvent used. A different solvent, or sometimes a mixture of solvents, can be used.

- The result of a chromatography experiment is called a **chromatogram**.

- The chromatogram shown above would indicate that there are three components in the mixture. However, there may be more but they did not separate well in the solvent used.

Chromatography can be used to identify specific components in dyes and food colourings. A sample of the unknown is run on a larger piece of chromatography paper with pure samples of the suspected dyes. The diagram on page 11 shows such a chromatogram.

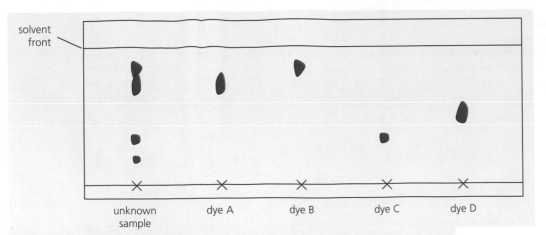

solvent
front

unknown sample   dye A   dye B   dye C   dye D

↑ **A typical chromatogram**

● The spots for the unknown sample can be compared with the spots for the pure dyes A, B, C and D.

● The unknown sample appears to have four different components, though the separation of the spots nearest the solvent front is not complete. A different solvent, or a mixture of solvents, could be used or the solvent could have been allowed to run further up the paper to achieve better separation.

From the chromatogram it is possible to state the following:

● The unknown sample is made up of a minimum of four different components.

● The unknown sample is a mixture of dyes A, B and C but *not* dye D.

● Dye B is the most soluble in the solvent because it moves furthest up the chromatography paper.

● One component in the unknown sample has not been identified.

Paper chromatography can be used to separate the components in a dye, a food colouring or a chemical indicator. If the substances to be separated are not coloured then the spots can be viewed under ultraviolet light – the spots can be drawn round in pencil while under ultraviolet light. Alternatively, a chemical developing agent can be sprayed on the chromatogram to mark the position of the spots by making them coloured. If the chemical in the spot is required, the spot can be cut out and the substance extracted from the paper by placing it in the solvent. The solvent can then be evaporated.

Planning methods of separation

Examination questions give examples of mixtures and you will be expected to decide on the most appropriate method of separating the components. The first thing to do is decide on the type of mixture and then choose the appropriate method of separation. Note that methods sometimes need to be combined to achieve a full separation.

Methods of separating mixtures

Components	Most suitable method of separation	Examples	Separation based on difference in this physical property
Insoluble solid and a liquid	Filtration	• Sand and water • Sulfur and water	Solubility in water
Soluble solid and the liquid in which it is dissolved	Simple distillation to obtain liquid	• Salt solution • Sugar solution	Boiling points
Soluble solid and the liquid in which it is dissolved	Recrystallisation to obtain the solid	• Salt solution • Sugar solution	Boiling points
Miscible liquids	Fractional distillation (can use simple distillation if boiling points differ substantially)	• Ethanol and water • Crude oil • Liquid air	Boiling points
Immiscible liquids	Separating funnel	• Oil and water	Density
Soluble substances	Chromatography	• Dyes • Food colourings • Chemical indicators	Solubility in solvent
Two solids – one magnetic and one non-magnetic	Magnetism	• Iron and sulfur • Aluminium and iron	Ability to be attracted by a magnet
Two solids – one soluble in water, the other insoluble	1 Dissolve in water 2 Filtration to obtain the insoluble solid 3 Recrystallisation to obtain the soluble solid from the filtrate	• Sand and salt • Sulfur and sugar	Solubility (filtration) Boiling points (recrystallisation)

Detection, analysis and identification

Revised

Elements and compounds in a mixture can be separated, detected, analysed and identified using modern instrumental techniques. Two of these techniques are:

● high-performance liquid chromatography (HPLC)

● mass spectrometry.

HPLC is a type of chromatography that can separate components in some mixtures. The components are dissolved in a solvent and then injected into a chromatography column.

The components pass along a chromatography column and each component takes a specific time to pass through the column – the time spent in the column is called the **retention time**.

A pure substance will always have the same retention time if the HPLC is repeated under the same conditions. This allows identification of components in a mixture by comparing their retention times with those of known pure substances.

HPLC produces a trace of the signal from a detector against retention time as shown here.

> **Exam tip**
>
> You may be asked to label the axes on an HPLC trace or be asked what HPLC is.

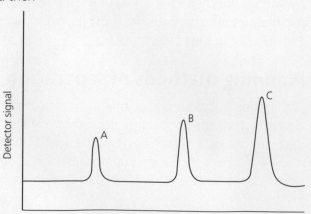

↑ **Typical HPLC trace**

1 Elements, Compounds and Mixtures

- The mixture that was analysed contained three components. Each is represented as a peak in the HPLC trace – A, B and C.
- Peak A has the shortest retention time and peak C has the longest retention time.

HPLC can also be used to check the purity of a sample because a pure substance should only produce one peak on an HPLC trace.

- HPLC is faster and provides better separation than other chromatography methods but it is expensive to operate, the speed of separation leads to a lack of sensitivity and trained staff are needed to operate it.

Mass spectrometry

Revised

Mass spectrometry is a technique that measures the masses of the particles in a substance. It can be used with elements and with compounds.

- The individual atoms of an element have a mass. The mass of these atoms is measured relative to a specific atom of carbon, which is given a mass number of 12 – this atom is called carbon-12. The mass number of an atom is a measure of its mass.
- Atoms of the same element can have different *mass* numbers – these are called isotopes (more detail on page 17).
- Mass spectrometry measures the proportion of each isotope in a sample of an element.
- This is plotted on a trace like the one shown here for a sample of chlorine. The trace shows the mass on the horizontal axis with the relative abundance on the vertical axis. The trace is called a **mass spectrum**.
- The relative atomic mass (RAM) of an element is the *average* mass of the atoms of an element based on the mass numbers of the atoms and their relative abundances.
- For chlorine, the mass spectrum trace shows that 75% of the atoms have a mass number of 35, and that the other 25% have a mass number of 37. This means in every 100 atoms, 75 atoms have a mass of 35 – the total mass of these atoms is 2625. And 25 atoms have a mass of 37 – the total mass of these atoms is 925. So the total mass of 100 chlorine atoms = 2625 + 925 = 3550; giving an average mass of $\frac{3550}{100}$ = 35.5. So, the relative atomic mass of chlorine is 35.5.

For a compound, the mass spectrum is much more complex as the compound can break up. The major peak with highest mass gives the relative molecular mass (RMM) of the compound.

The mass spectrum shown here is for ethanol, C_2H_5OH. The major peak with the highest mass is at a mass value of 46 so the RMM of the compound is 46.

The advantages of mass spectrometry are that the sample can be very small and that individual elements and compounds can be identified by comparison with data from known pure compounds.

The disadvantages are that impure samples are difficult to analyse, which can lead to false identification – also the equipment is expensive and trained staff are needed to operate it.

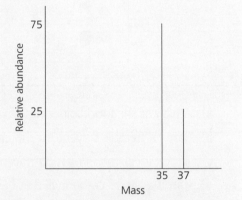

↑ A typical mass spectrum – this is for chlorine atoms

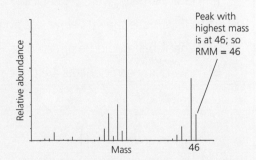

Peak with highest mass is at 46; so RMM = 46

↑ A typical mass spectrum for a compound

1 What is meant by these terms:

   a) element; **b)** atom; **c)** compound?   [3]

2 Plan a practical method for the separation of a mixture of sand and water.   [4]

3 State the methods of separation used for these mixtures:

   a) oil and water; **b)** iron and sulfur.   [2]

4 State one disadvantage of high-performance liquid chromatography.   [1]

5 State one advantage of mass spectrometry.   [1]

6 Explain what is meant by these terms:

   a) solute; **b)** solvent; **c)** solution.   [3]

7 This chromatogram was obtained for different food colourings labelled 1, 2, 3 and 4.

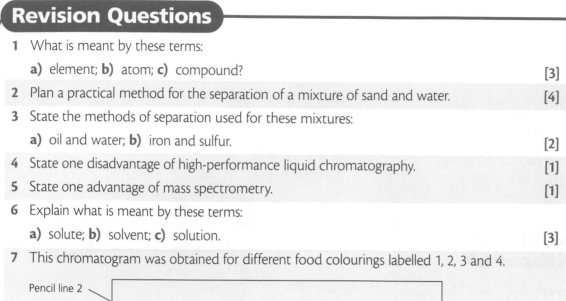

   a) Which of the food colourings is a pure substance?   [1]

   b) Name a suitable solvent for this chromatography.   [1]

   c) Which food colouring is composed of three components?   [1]

   d) State two food colourings that have a common component.   [1]

   e) Which food colouring has the component that is least soluble in the solvent?   [1]

   f) Suggest why a pencil is used to draw the horizontal lines on the chromatogram.   [1]

   g) What name is given to pencil line 2?   [1]

8 The HPLC trace shown below was obtained using a mixture.

   a) What label should be placed on the trace at Y?   [1]

   b) How many components are present in the mixture?   [1]

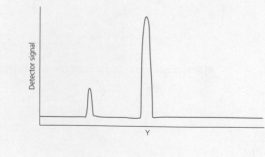

9 The diagram below shows a commonly used separation technique.

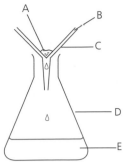

    a) What labels should be placed on the diagram at B, C and D? [3]

    b) What is the general name for the solid obtained at A? [1]

    c) What is the general name for the liquid obtained at E? [1]

    d) Name one mixture which could be separated in this way. [1]

10 State two physical properties of metals. [2]

11 Name the separation technique that would provide the best separation of a mixture of ethanol and water. [1]

12 Give examples of two immiscible liquids. [1]

Questions 13 to 15 relate to the trace obtained for a sample of boron using an analytical technique.

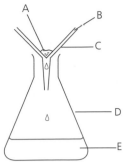

13 Name the analytical technique that produced this trace. [1]

14 How many isotopes of boron exist? [1]

15 Using the relative abundances and mass values, calculate the relative atomic mass of boron. [2]

Go online for the answers

Online

2 Atomic Structure and Bonding

● An **atom** is the simplest particle of an **element** that can exist on its own in a stable environment.

● Atoms are made up of three subatomic particles – **protons**, **neutrons** and **electrons**.

● Protons and neutrons are found in the **nucleus** (the centre of the atom) and electrons are found in **shells** orbiting the nucleus.

● The mass of an atom is largely in its nucleus because the mass of an electron is very small compared to a proton or a neutron.

● Atoms are **electrically neutral** (they have no charge). This is because they have equal numbers of protons and electrons. Protons have a positive charge and electrons have a negative charge.

● Neutrons do not have a charge.

The table below gives the relative masses and relative charges of the three subatomic particles.

Subatomic particles

Subatomic particle	Relative mass	Relative charge	Location
Proton	1	+1	Nucleus
Neutron	1	0	Nucleus
Electron	$\frac{1}{1840}$	−1	Shells

Atomic number and mass number   Revised

The **atomic number** is used to order the elements in the Periodic Table.

● The atomic number is also called the **proton number** because it tells us the number of protons in the nucleus of an atom.

● The **mass number** of an atom is the total number of protons and neutrons in its nucleus. (The electron mass is so small that it does not affect the mass number.)

The atomic number and mass number of an atom are usually written before the symbol of the element. The mass number is at the top and the atomic number is at the bottom – for example $^{12}_{6}C$, $^{39}_{19}K$, $^{35}_{17}Cl$, $^{31}_{15}P$, $^{27}_{13}Al$.

Determining numbers of subatomic particles

The numbers of subatomic particles **in an atom** can be determined from the atomic number and the mass number:

● number of protons = atomic number

● number of neutrons = mass number − atomic number

● number of electrons = number of protons

Example 1

Determine the number of each subatomic particle in each of the following atoms:

a) $_{6}^{12}C$ atomic number = 6 (**6 protons**)

              6 electrons because it is an atom

              mass number – atomic number = 12 – 6 = 6 (**6 neutrons**)

b) $_{19}^{39}K$ atomic number = 19 (**19 protons**)

              19 electrons because it is an atom

              mass number – atomic number = 39 – 19 = 20 (**20 neutrons**)

c) $_{17}^{35}Cl$ atomic number = 17 (**17 protons**)

              17 electrons because it is an atom

              mass number – atomic number = 35 – 17 = 18 (**18 neutrons**)

> **Exam tip**
>
> Remember that atoms have the *same number* of protons and electrons. They do not have the same number of protons and neutrons. ($_{6}^{12}C$ does but this is not always the case.)

You can be asked to identify a particular isotope from the numbers of subatomic particles – for example, identify a particle that has 9 protons, 9 electrons and 10 neutrons:

- 9 protons means that the atomic number is 9, so it is a particle of fluorine.
- 9 protons and 9 electrons means that it is an atom, so it is an atom of fluorine.
- 9 protons and 10 neutrons means that its mass number is 9 + 10 = 19.
- The atom is $_{9}^{19}F$.

Isotopes and relative atomic mass

Revised

There are two types of chlorine atom and they have different mass numbers – $_{17}^{35}Cl$ and $_{17}^{37}Cl$. There are three types of hydrogen atom with different mass numbers – $_{1}^{1}H$, $_{1}^{2}H$, $_{1}^{3}H$. Atoms of the same element that have different mass numbers are called isotopes. **Isotopes** are atoms that have the same number of protons but different numbers of neutrons.

The two isotopes of chlorine, $_{17}^{35}Cl$ and $_{17}^{37}Cl$ (often called chlorine-35 and chlorine-37), are both chlorine atoms and both have the properties of chlorine atoms.

The mass of a chlorine atom in a sample of chlorine is an average of the masses of chlorine-35 and chlorine-37 atoms. Only one-quarter of chlorine atoms are chlorine-37 with three-quarters of them chlorine-35 – so the average mass of a chlorine atom works out at 35.5.

If you had 100 chlorine atoms, 75 would have a mass of 35 and 25 would have a mass of 37. The average mass of a chlorine atom is calculated like this:

$$\text{average mass} = \frac{(75 \times 35) + (25 \times 37)}{100} = 35.5$$

This average mass is called the **relative atomic mass** of chlorine (page 13). The word 'relative' is used because the masses of all atoms are measured relative to the mass of an atom of carbon-12.

> **Exam tip**
>
> Being asked to define the term 'isotopes' is a common question. Remember that there are three main parts to the definition – 'Isotopes are *atoms* with the *same atomic number* (or the same number of protons) but with *different mass numbers* (or different numbers of neutrons)'.

History of development of atomic theory

Ideas about the structure of atoms have changed over time as new research was carried out, new technologies became available and scientists used the knowledge to develop new theories about the atom. All this work has resulted in the model of the atom we use today.

- Early 1800s – John Dalton stated that atoms were the smallest particles of matter.
- In 1897 – J. J. Thomson proposed the 'plum pudding' model which states that the negative electrons were embedded in a positive sphere (like the raisins in a plum pudding).
- In 1911 – Ernest Rutherford revised Thomson's model in which the electrons orbit a positive nucleus.
- 1932 – James Chadwick discovered the neutron. It was discovered after the other subatomic particles because it was more difficult to detect as it has no charge.

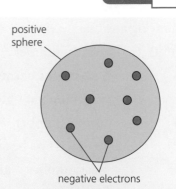

↑ **Plum pudding model of the atom**

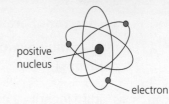

↑ **Rutherford's model of the atom**

Electronic configuration

The arrangement of electrons in the shells around the nucleus can be represented either by a diagram or in written format. You will need to remember the following rules as to where the electrons can be:

1 The shells are at increasing distances from the central nucleus. The shell closest to the nucleus is called the first shell – then there are the second, third and fourth shells.

2 The first shell can hold a maximum of 2 electrons.

3 The second and third shells can hold a maximum of 8 electrons.

4 The first shell must fill first, before an electron can be put into the second shell; and the second shell must fill before an electron can be put into the third shell, and so on.

5 Electrons pair up in the shells but only when no other space is available. For example, four electrons in shell 2 would not pair up; but six electrons would have two pairs with the other two electrons unpaired. The two electrons in the first shell must be paired as it can only hold a maximum of two.

In many diagrams, '×' is used to represent an electron.

Example 2

Lithium has atomic number 3, so an atom of lithium has 3 electrons.

The first shell takes 2 electrons (paired) and 1 electron goes into the second shell.

The written electronic configuration of lithium is 2,1.

The electronic configuration of lithium is shown here.

> **Exam tip**
>
> When a question asks you to draw a diagram of an atom, you must write the correct number of protons and neutrons in the nucleus and the correct number and arrangement of electrons in the shells. These questions can be worth up to 4 marks.

> **Exam tip**
>
> If you are asked to show an electronic configuration, read the question twice to check if it has asked for the diagram form or the written form. If the question says 'draw', then make sure you do! If the question does not specify which then the written form is acceptable.

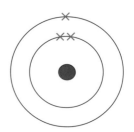

↑ **Electronic configuration of lithium**

Example 3

Sulfur has atomic number 16, so an atom of sulfur has 16 electrons. The first shell takes 2 electrons, the second shell takes 8 electrons (four pairs) and the third shell takes 6 electrons (two pairs and two singles).

The written electronic configuration of sulfur is 2,8,6.

The drawn electronic configuration of sulfur is shown here.

The written and drawn electronic configurations for atoms of elements with atomic numbers 1 to 20 are shown in the table.

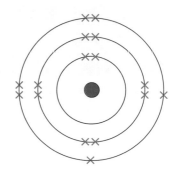

⬆ Electronic configuration of sulfur

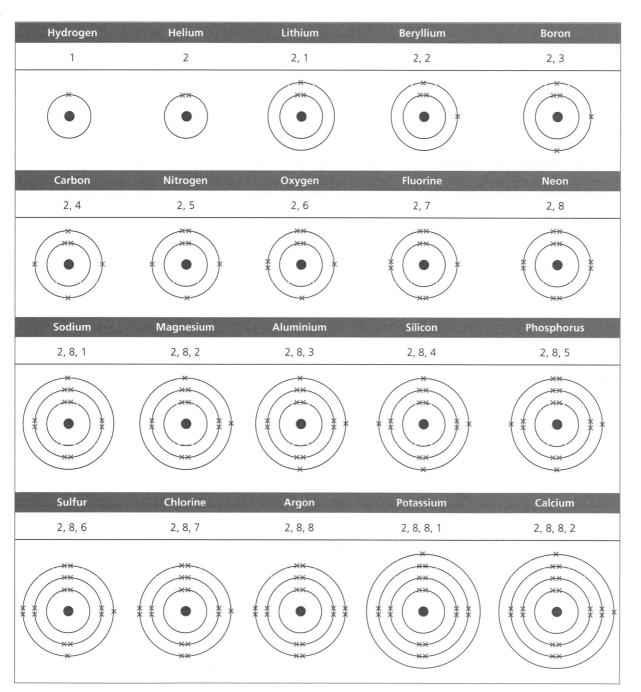

⬆ Electronic configurations of elements 1–20

Electronic configuration from the Periodic Table

The electronic configuration of an atom can be determined from the Periodic Table by using the group number and the period number:

● the group number gives the number of electrons in the outer shell.

● the period number gives the number of shells in use.

Example 4

What is the electronic configuration of an atom of potassium?

Potassium is in Period 4 – that means four shells in use:

  –,–,–,–.

The element is in Group 1 – that means one electron in the outer shell:

  –,–,–,1.

The three inner shells must be full (see rule 4 on page 18).

So the electronic configuration of an atom of potassium must be **2,8,8,1**.

Example 5

What is the electronic configuration of an atom of nitrogen?

Nitrogen is in Period 2 – that means two shells in use:

  –,–.

The element is in Group 5 – that means five electrons in the outer shell:

  –,5.

The inner shell must be full.

So the electronic configuration of an atom of nitrogen must be **2,5**.

Noble gases

The noble gases all have full outer shells:

● helium, He: 2

● neon, Ne: 2, 8

● argon, Ar: 2, 8, 8

A full outer shell is stable and this makes the noble gases unreactive.

Ions

An ion is a charged particle:

● a positive ion is called a **cation**

● a negative ion is called an **anion**.

A simple ion is formed when an atom loses or gains electrons to achieve a full outer shell. The overall charge on an ion depends on the number of positive protons and the number of negative electrons.

Simple positive ions have the same name as the atom from which they are formed – for example, a hydrogen ion is H^+, a sodium ion is Na^+ and a magnesium ion is Mg^{2+}.

Simple negative ions change their ending to '**-ide**' – for example, chlorine forms chloride ions (Cl^-) and oxygen forms oxide ions (O^{2-}).

Example 6

Determine the numbers of protons and electrons, and the electronic configuration of an oxide ion, O^{2-}.

- The atomic number of oxygen is 8, so there are **8 protons**.

- An atom of oxygen would have 8 electrons, but the ion has a 2– charge so it has two extra electrons making **10 electrons**.

- The electronic configuration of the oxide ion is **2,8**.

Example 7

Write the formula, including the charge, of the simple ion that has 13 protons and has the electronic configuration 2,8.

- 13 protons means atomic number 13, so it is an ion of aluminium.

- The electronic configuration 2,8 means there are **10 electrons**.

- 13 positive protons and 10 negative electrons make +13 − 10 = +3, so the ion has charge of **3+**.

- It is an aluminium ion, **Al^{3+}**

Exam tip

There are two main type of examination questions:

- those that ask you to determine the number of each subatomic particle in an ion

- those that ask you to to work out the formula of the ion, including its charge, from the number of the subatomic particles.

Exam tip

This type of question is often given in table form. All the data may be given and the identity of the particles asked, or some data may be missing and you are asked to fill in the missing information. Letters are used to represent atoms and ions but you will be reminded that these are not the symbols of elements. Remember that the electronic configuration does not give you the identity of the atom or ion – it must be the number of protons or the atomic number.

Worked example 1

a) Fill in the missing information in the table. [3]

Particle	Atomic number	Mass number	Number of protons	Number of neutrons	Number of electrons	Electronic configuration
A	12	24				2,8
B			18	22	18	
C	7			7		2,8

b) Identify A, B and C and include the charge on any ions. [3]

Answers

a)

Particle	Atomic number	Mass number	Number of protons	Number of neutrons	Number of electrons	Electronic configuration
A	12	24	**12**	**12**	**10**	2,8
B	**18**	**40**	18	22	18	**2,8,8**
C	7	**14**	**7**	7	**10**	2,8

[1] for each correct row

b) For A, the atomic number = 12 so it is a magnesium particle. The number of protons = 12. The number of electrons = 10. So it is a **magnesium ion, Mg^{2+}** [1]

For B, the atomic number = 18 so it is an argon particle. The number of protons = 18. The number of electrons = 18. So it is an **argon atom, Ar** [1]

For C, the atomic number = 7 so it is a nitrogen particle. The number of protons = 7. The number of electrons = 10. So it is a **nitride ion, N^{3-}** [1]

Bonding

Revised

The way in which molecules and structures are held together is called **bonding**. There are three main types of bonding – **ionic**, **covalent** and **metallic**.

- Ionic bonding occurs in compounds composed of a metal and a non-metal – such as sodium chloride and magnesium oxide.
- Covalent bonding occurs between non-metal atoms – this can be in compounds such as hydrogen chloride and water, or in elements such as chlorine (Cl_2) and carbon (graphite).
- Metallic bonding occurs in metals.

All bonding involves electrons and these are usually represented by dots (•) or crosses (✗) in bonding diagrams – these are called **dot and cross diagrams**. Remember that all electrons are the same – using dots and crosses shows which atoms the electrons come from.

Ionic bonding

Ionic compounds are compounds which contain a metal – they are said to have ionic bonding. Examples are sodium chloride (NaCl), magnesium oxide (MgO), calcium chloride ($CaCl_2$), potassium sulfide (K_2S) and lithium fluoride (LiF).

- Ionic compounds are made up of ions. **Ions are charged particles**.
- An ionic compound contains **positive ions** and **negative ions**.
- Simple ions are those formed when an atom of an element gains or loses electrons – e.g. Na^+, O^{2-}, Al^{3+} and Br^-.
- Molecular ions are charged particles that contain more than one atom. The molecular ions required are given on the *Data Leaflet* – they include the ammonium ion, NH_4^+, sulfate ion, SO_4^{2-}, hydroxide ion, OH^- and nitrate ion, NO_3^-.
- The hydroxide is the only molecular ion you need to know that ends in -ide. All other ions that end in -ide are simple negatively charged ions.

Formation of ions from atoms

When an ionic compound forms from the atoms of its elements, a **transfer of electrons** occurs. Metal atoms lose electrons and give them to non-metal atoms, which accept electrons. Each will lose or gain enough electrons to form a full outer shell and make it more stable:

● when a metal atom loses electrons, it becomes a positively charged ion

● when a non-metal atom gains electrons, it becomes a negatively charged ion.

You can be asked to show the formation of an ionic compound from the atoms of the elements it is made up of. These compounds will contain either a Group 1 or Group 2 metal (Li, Na, K, Mg or Ca) with a Group 6 or Group 7 non-metal (O, S, F or Cl). Beryllium will not be used because its chemistry is unusual.

There are four possible combinations:

● a Group 1 metal with Group 7 non-metal – e.g. NaCl, KF, NaF, KCl, LiCl, LiF

● a Group 2 metal with Group 7 non-metal – e.g. $CaCl_2$, $MgCl_2$, CaF_2, MgF_2

● a Group 1 metal with Group 6 non-metal – e.g. K_2S, Na_2O, Na_2S, K_2O, Li_2O, Li_2S

● a Group 2 metal with Group 6 non-metal – e.g. MgO, CaO, MgS, CaS.

Example 8: Sodium chloride

A sodium atom has an electronic configuration of 2,8,1.

When it react with a chlorine atom (electronic configuration 2,8,7), the one outer electron of the sodium atom is transferred to the outer shell of the chlorine atom.

Each sodium now has only 10 electrons (2,8) but it has 11 protons in its nucleus, so it has charge 1+.

The sodium atom is written 'Na'; the sodium ion formed is written 'Na^+'.

Simple positive ions have the same name as the atom – so Na^+ is called a **sodium ion**.

Each chlorine now has 18 electrons (2,8,8) but it has 17 protons in its nucleus so it has charge 1−.

The chlorine atom is written 'Cl'; the chloride ion formed is written 'Cl^-'.

Simple negative ions change the end of their name to **-ide**, so it is called a **chloride ion**.

The sodium ions and chloride ions are attracted to each other and form an **ionic compound**.

The ionic bond is the attraction between oppositely charged ions in an ionic compound.

The dot and cross diagram below summarises the process of ion formation in sodium chloride.

Exam tip

● Remember that ionic compounds do not have a charge – but ions do have a charge.

● When an ion has a single positive charge, it is correct to write this as '+'. Do not write '1+' or '+1'. Similarly when an ion has a single negative charge, write this as '−', not '1−' or '−1'.

● For ions with a higher charge, always write these in the same way as those on the back of the *Data Leaflet* – for example 2+ (*not* +2); 3− (*not* −3).

Exam tip

● Questions often ask about the electronic configurations of atoms and of ions. The electronic configuration of the Na^+ ion is 2,8 but this is the same as the electronic configuration of a Ne atom. The difference is the number of protons in the nucleus. The number of electrons can help to identify an unknown atom but be careful if it is an ion because it will have lost or gained electrons. You can work out how many it has lost or gained from its charge.

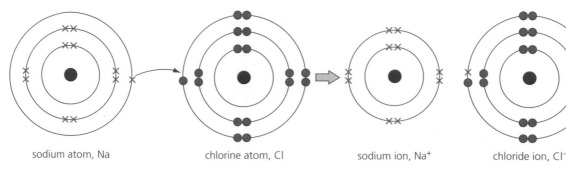

| sodium atom, Na | chlorine atom, Cl | sodium ion, Na⁺ | chloride ion, Cl⁻ |

↑ Ion formation in sodium chloride, NaCl

The compound formed is called **sodium chloride** (because it contains sodium ions and chloride ions). There is a lot of information here that helps in working out the **formula** of the compound. Each sodium atom loses 1 electron and each chlorine atom gains 1 electron, so only one atom of each is required and the formula of sodium chloride is **NaCl**. Because a sodium ion is Na^+ and a chloride ion is Cl^-, only one ion of each is required so that the compound has no overall charge.

Exam tip
● When showing the formation of an ionic compound, always use dots and crosses to make it clear where the transferred electrons are coming from and where they are going to. In Example 8 you can see that a sodium electron ends up in a chloride ion. Make sure the charges on the ions are shown and that the numbers of each ion present match up.

Example 9: Calcium chloride

Two chlorine atoms are required for each calcium atom because each calcium atom loses 2 electrons and each chlorine atom gains 1 electron.

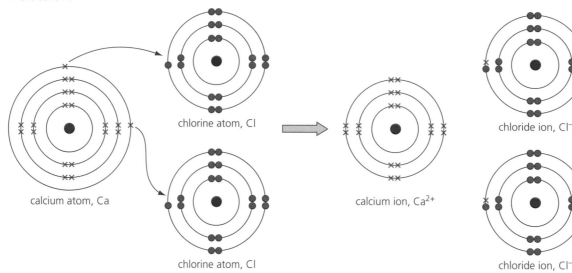

↑ Ion formation in calcium chloride, $CaCl_2$

A calcium ion is Ca^{2+} because it has only 18 electrons but 20 protons (atomic number = 20).

Chloride ions are Cl^- as described earlier. The formula of calcium chloride is **$CaCl_2$**.

Example 10: Magnesium oxide

Only one magnesium atom is required for each oxygen atom because each magnesium atom loses 2 electrons and each oxygen atom gains 2 electrons.

Exam tip
● Always write the ionic bond description ('the ionic bond is the attraction between oppositely charged ions') at the end of an ionic bonding dot and cross diagram.

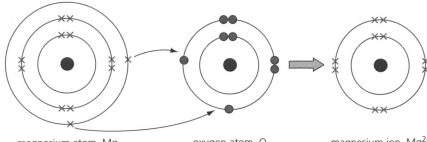
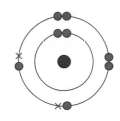

| magnesium atom, Mg | oxygen atom, O | magnesium ion, Mg²⁺ | oxide ion, O²⁻ |

↑ Ion formation in magnesium oxide, MgO

A magnesium ion is Mg^{2+} as it has only 10 electrons (2,8) but 12 protons (atomic number = 12).

An oxide ion is O^{2-} because it has 10 electrons (2,8) but only 8 protons (atomic number = 8). The formula of magnesium oxide is **MgO**.

Example 11: Potassium sulfide

Two potassium atoms are needed for each sulfur atom because each potassium atom loses 1 electron and each sulfur atom gains 2 electrons.

Exam tip
● The charge on a simple ion can be checked by looking at the group number of the element. Group 1 elements form ions with a + charge; Group 2 form 2+ ions; Group 3 form 3+ ions; Group 4 do not generally form ions. Group 5 form ions with a 3– charge; Group 6 ions have a 2– charge and Group 7 form ions with a – charge. Group 0 do not form ions because they have full outer shells.

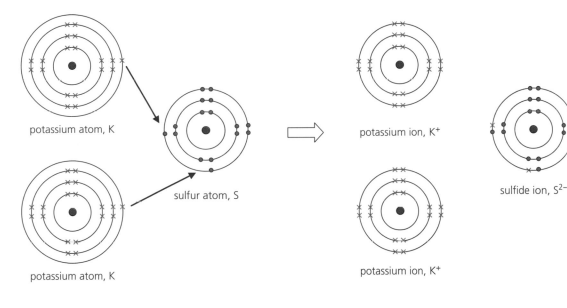

↑ Ion formation in potassium sulfide, K₂S

A potassium ion is K^{+} because it has only 18 electrons (2,8,8) but 19 protons (atomic number = 19).

A sulfide ion is S^{2-} because it has 18 electrons (2,8,8) but only 16 protons (atomic number = 16).

The formula of potassium sulfide is **K₂S**.

Exam tip
● If you are asked to show all the subatomic particles in an atom or ion, label the nucleus and write how many protons and neutrons are present.

It is important to understand the structure of a substance as well as its bonding.

● Bonding and structure are **not** the same. A substance can be covalently bonded but it may have a simple structure or a giant structure.

● Structure and bonding are used to explain many of the properties of substances.

Ionic bonding

● An ionic bond is the attraction between oppositely charged ions.

● Ionic compounds have a structure described as an **ionic lattice**.

● The ionic lattice is a three-dimensional network of positive ions and negative ions held together by the ionic bonds (electrostatic forces) between the oppositely charged ions.

Properties of ionic compounds

Ionic bonds are strong and it is these bonds that give ionic compounds their properties.

● In their normal solid state, ionic compounds cannot conduct electricity because the ions (charged particles) cannot move and carry charge.

● When an ionic compound is melted (it is described as **molten**) the ions can move and carry charge, so molten ionic compounds conduct electricity.

● Most ionic compounds dissolve in water.

● When an ionic compound dissolves in water (it is described as **aqueous**) the ions can move and carry charge, so aqueous ionic compounds conduct electricity.

● Ionic compounds have high melting points and boiling points and are all solids at room temperature and pressure because substantial energy is required to break the strong ionic bonds between the ions.

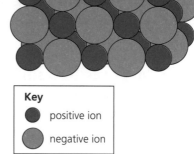

Key
● positive ion
● negative ion

↑ **An ionic lattice structure**

Exam tip

Learn the properties of ionic compounds carefully. A question can ask you to identify the type of an unknown compound just from its properties. If it has a high melting point and does not conduct electricity when solid but does when molten or dissolved in water then it is an ionic compound.

Covalent bonding

A **covalent bond** is formed between non-metal atoms. A single covalent bond is formed by a **shared pair of electrons**.

There are several non-metallic elements that are **diatomic**, which means they exist as molecules containing two atoms covalently bonded together. The element should be written with a small '$_2$' after the symbol, for example H_2.

The diatomic elements are H_2, N_2, O_2, F_2, Cl_2, Br_2 and I_2. So, the symbol for chlorine is written 'Cl', but the element chlorine should be written 'Cl_2'.

Hydrogen molecules contain a single covalent bond between the hydrogen atoms involving a shared pair of electrons. One electron comes from each H atom as shown here.

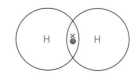

↑ **Hydrogen, a diatomic element**

The covalent bond in hydrogen molecules can be shown as H—H, where the long dash represents the single covalent bond.

If two pairs of electrons are shared between two non-metal atoms, this is a double **covalent bond**. This is represented by a double dash, e.g. O=O.

A triple covalent bond (three shared pairs of electrons) is shown as a triple dash between the atoms, e.g. N≡N.

Non-metal atoms share electrons to complete their outer shells.

Note: *It is important to understand that shared electrons count as outer shell electrons for both atoms.*

Here are some dot and cross diagrams showing molecules with only single covalent bonds.

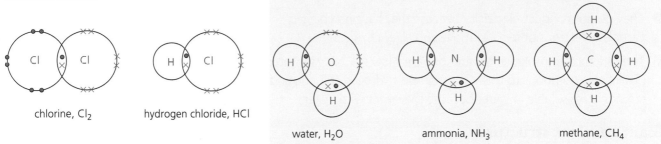

chlorine, Cl_2 hydrogen chloride, HCl   water, H_2O ammonia, NH_3 methane, CH_4

↑ **Substances with single covalent bonds**

A pair of electrons that are part of a covalent bond is called a **bonding pair of electrons**. A pair of electrons that are not involved in a bond is called a **lone pair of electrons**. You need to be able to label lone pairs of electrons.

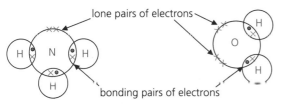

lone pairs of electrons

bonding pairs of electrons

↑ **Lone pairs and bonding pairs of electrons**

Here are some dot and cross diagrams showing molecules with multiple (double and triple) covalent bonds.

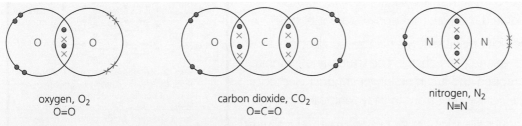

oxygen, O_2
O=O

carbon dioxide, CO_2
O=C=O

nitrogen, N_2
N≡N

↑ **Substances with multiple covalent bonds**

All of the molecules shown are called simple covalent molecules and their structure is described as **molecular** or **simple**.

Chlorine and oxygen are examples of simple covalent elements – they are **diatomic**.

Water, methane, ammonia and carbon dioxide are examples of simple covalent compounds.

Properties of simple covalent substances

Simple covalent substances have weak forces of attraction between their molecules.

These weak forces of attractions are called **van der Waals' forces** of attraction. The physical properties of simple covalent substances depend on the weak van der Waals' forces of attraction.

The physical properties of simple covalent substances are:

● They have low melting and boiling points because little energy is required to break the weak forces of attraction between the molecules.

● They are gases, liquids or low melting point solids at room temperature.

● They do not conduct electricity because they have no charged particles (electrons or ions) to move and carry charge.

● They are mostly insoluble in water or have a low solubility in water. (There are exceptions to this – for example hydrogen chloride and ammonia are soluble in water because they react with water.)

Giant covalent structures

Some covalently bonded substances have **giant structures**.

● Diamond and graphite are both forms of the element carbon.

● Diamond and graphite have giant covalent structures.

● Different forms of the same element in the same physical state are called **allotropes**.

● Diamond and graphite are allotropes of carbon.

Properties of giant covalent substances

Covalent bonds are strong and substantial energy is required to break them.

The large number of very strong covalent bonds in giant covalent substances can be used to explain their properties.

● Both diamond and graphite have very high melting points (and boiling points) and are solids at room temperature and pressure because substantial energy is required to break the strong covalent bonds.

● Graphite conducts electricity because it has delocalised electrons in its structure which can move and carry charge. The structure of graphite is disrupted when it is molten and it can no longer conduct electricity because there are no delocalised electrons to move and carry charge.

● Diamond does not conduct electricity as it does not have delocalised electrons.

● Graphite can act as a lubricant because the layers can slide over each other. This also explains its use in pencils – layers slide off when the pencil is moved against paper.

● Both diamond and graphite are insoluble in water.

● Diamond is the hardest naturally occurring substance on Earth. This is caused by the strong covalent bonds throughout the rigid tetrahedral lattice structure.

● Diamond is used in cutting tools (like drill tips and saws) as it is so hard and can drill though rock and cut through metals.

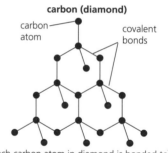
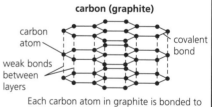

Metallic bonding

The bonding in a metal is caused by the attraction between delocalised electrons and the positive ions in the structure of the metal.

The ions are arranged in layers, as shown in the diagram, with the delocalised electrons moving between the layers.

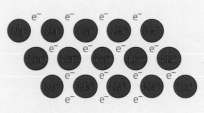

↑ Metallic bonding

Properties of metals

The structure and bonding of metals are used to explain their properties.

- Metals (mostly) have high melting points and are normally solids (except mercury) because substantial energy is required to overcome the strong metallic bonds between the positive ions and the delocalised electrons.
- Metals conduct electricity because the delocalised electrons can move and carry charge.
- When metals are molten they will still conduct electricity because the electrons are still delocalised and can move and carry charge.
- Metals are **malleable** (can be hammered into shape) and **ductile** (can be drawn out into wires) because the layers of ions can slide over each other without disrupting the bonding.
- An **alloy** is a mixture of two or more elements, at least one of which is a metal. An alloy will have metallic properties but the properties are often better than the original metal(s) from which it was formed; for example, stainless steel is an alloy of iron with chromium and it does not rust easily, unlike steel.

Uses of metals

- Aluminium is used for making overhead power cables because it has a low density and is a good conductor of electricity. It is also used for alloys for aircraft manufacture because of its low density.
- Copper is used for electrical wiring because it is a good conductor of electricity and is ductile; it is also used for plumbing because it is malleable. Copper is also used to manufacture brass and is the main metal in 'copper' coins.
- Iron is used for bridges and structures because it is a strong metal.
- Magnesium is used in flares because it burns with a bright white light. It is also used in high strength alloys for aircraft because of its low density.

Exam tip

Familiarise yourself with the properties of ionic compounds, simple covalent substances, giant covalent substances and metals – particularly to do with melting point (and boiling point) and whether or not they conduct electricity. This information can be vital in identifying the type of an unknown substance.

Exam tip

Often questions about uses will relate the use to the property on which that use depends. Make sure you can choose the correct property related to the use.

Worked example 2

The table below gives information on four substances – A, B, C and D. The letters A, B, C and D do not represent the symbols of elements.

Substance	Melting point /°C	Electrical conductivity of solid substance	Electrical conductivity of molten substance
A	2800	Poor	Good
B	−7	Poor	Poor
C	660	Good	Good
D	3500	Good	Poor

Which substance is likely to be: **a)** a metal; **b)** an ionic compound; **c)** graphite; **d)** a simple covalent substance?   [4]

Answers
a) C [1]; **b)** A [1]; **c)** D [1]; **d)** B [1]

Exam tip

This type of question is common and it is vital to remember the properties of all four types of substance. If you can't recall them, look again at pages 26 to 29.

1 What is meant by the term 'atomic number'? [1]

2 State the relative mass and relative charge of: **a)** a proton; **b)** an electron; **c)** a neutron. [3]

3 ^{35}Cl and ^{37}Cl are isotopes of chlorine. What is meant by the term 'isotopes'? [1]

4 Draw and write electronic configurations for these atoms:

   a) P; **b)** Li; **c)** O; **d)** K; **e)** Ar; **f)** He; **g)** Al; **h)** Na [8]

5 Write electronic configurations for these ions:

   a) Na^+; **b)** F^-; **c)** Al^{3+}; **d)** O^{2-}; **e)** K^+ [5]

6 Sodium chloride conducts electricity when it is molten, but not when it is a solid. Explain why. [3]

7 Explain how a single covalent bond is formed. [2]

8 Draw a diagram to show the bonding in the following molecules – only outer shell electrons need to be shown:

   a) Cl_2 [2]; **b)** H_2O [3]; **c)** CO_2 [3]

9 Chlorine boils at −34 °C. Explain why chlorine has a low boiling point. [3]

10 Draw a diagram to show the bonding and structure in diamond. [3]

11 Explain why graphite conducts electricity. [3]

12 What is meant by the term malleable? [1]

13 Describe the structure and bonding in a metal like sodium. [3]

14 Draw a labelled diagram of a calcium atom, $^{40}_{20}$Ca, showing the numbers of all subatomic particles. [4]

15 Complete the table below for each of the particles X, Y and Z. The particles may be atoms or they may be ions. The letters X, Y and Z do not represent symbols for elements. [3]

Particle	Atomic number	Mass number	Number of protons	Number of neutrons	Number of electrons	Electronic configuration
X			11	12		2,8
Y	17			18	17	
Z		16	8		10	

3 Formulae and Equations

Note: *The skills of writing formulae and equations are required in C1 and C2.*

To be able to work out the **formula** of a compound, you need to use **valencies**.

'Valency' is the combining power of an element or an ion. It can be worked out from the Group number of the elements as shown in this table.

Note that elements in Group 0 do not form compounds, so they have no valency. Hydrogen always has a valency of 1.

The valency is also the same as the charge on ions. The way in which atoms become ions has been covered earlier. Molecular ions have the valencies as shown in the table. These are the same as the size of the charge on the molecular ion.

Valency and group number

Group	Valency
1	1
2	2
3	3
4	4
5	3
6	2
7	1
0	none

The valencies of some molecular ions

Name	Formula	Valency
Ammonium	NH_4^+	1
Carbonate	CO_3^{2-}	2
Dichromate	$Cr_2O_7^{2-}$	2
Ethanoate	CH_3COO^-	1
Hydrogen carbonate	HCO_3^-	1
Hydroxide	OH^-	1
Methanoate	$HCOO^-$	1
Nitrate	NO_3^-	1
Sulfate	SO_4^{2-}	2
Sulfite	SO_3^{2-}	2

The valency of a **transition metal** (elements in the middle block in the Periodic Table – see page 39) is given in roman numerals after the name of the element.

The valencies of some transition elements

Transition metal	Valency of metal
iron(II) compounds	2
iron(III) compounds	3
copper(II) compounds	2
cobalt(II) compounds	2
silver(I) compounds	1

> **Exam tip**
>
> For unfamiliar ions, the valency is the same as the charge. For example, the thiosulfate ion, $S_2O_3^{2-}$, has a valency of 2; the Cu^+ ion has a valency of 1.

> **Exam tip**
>
> Transition metal ions without a roman numeral in their name usually have a valency of 2. The copper in 'copper sulfate' has a valency of 2; the zinc in 'zinc chloride' has a valency of 2. This is important because some exam questions do not give the roman numeral. The only exception to this in GCSE Chemistry is silver compounds, in which the silver has a valency of 1.

How to work out the formula of a compound

Revised

The formula of a compound can be determined using valencies by the following method.

1 Compound name   potassium chloride

2 Convert to symbols   K   Cl

3 Look up the valencies   1 (in Group 1)   1 (in Group 7)

4 Write the valencies above symbols $\overset{1}{K}$ $\overset{1}{Cl}$

5 Cancel down if necessary

Not needed in this case but for example $\overset{2}{Mg}$ $\overset{2}{O}$ becomes $\overset{1}{Mg}$ $\overset{1}{O}$

Note: *This is the step most often forgotten.*

6 Cross-over $\overset{1}{K}\overset{\longleftarrow}{}\overset{1}{Cl}$

7 Write with crossed-over numbers K_1Cl_1

(Use brackets here if a molecular ion is multiplied by 2 or more)

8 Ignore the '1's (so $K_1 = K$)   KCl

Example 1

Use the method shown above to work out the formulae of these compounds:

Exam tip

A chemical formula is like a word so keep all the letters and numbers close with no spaces.

a) Magnesium chloride   Mg   Cl

            Valency   2   1

                  $\overset{2}{Mg}\overset{\longleftarrow}{}\overset{1}{Cl}$ No cancel / Cross over

                   Mg_1Cl_2 **MgCl₂**

b) Calcium oxide   Ca   O

            Valency   2   2

                  $\overset{2}{Ca}$ $\overset{2}{O}$ Cancel down / Cross over

                  $\overset{1}{Ca}\overset{\longleftarrow}{}\overset{1}{O}$

                   Ca_1O_1 **CaO**

c) Iron(III) chloride   Fe   Cl

            Valency   3   1   No cancel / Cross over

                  $\overset{3}{Fe}\overset{\longleftarrow}{}\overset{1}{Cl}$

                   Fe_1Cl_3 **FeCl₃**

d) Calcium hydroxide   Ca   OH

            Valency   2   1   No cancel / Cross over

                  $\overset{2}{Ca}\overset{\longleftarrow}{}\overset{1}{OH}$

                   $Ca_1(OH)_2$ **Ca(OH)₂**

32

3 Formulae and Equations

Covalent compounds are compounds containing only non-metals. So we cannot use ions to determine the formulae of covalent compounds, but the rules of valency still apply.

Note: *Hydrogen, H, always has a valency of 1.*

Example 2
Use the valency method to work out the formulae of the following compounds:

a) methane (C and H)

$$\overset{4}{C} \overset{1}{H} \quad CH_4$$

b) ammonia (N and H)

$$\overset{3}{N} \overset{1}{H} \quad NH_3$$

c) water (H and O)

$$\overset{1}{H} \overset{2}{O} \quad H_2O$$

Exam tip

The formulae of some compounds do not need working out. For example, carbon dioxide is CO_2 – the 'di' indicates 2 oxygen atoms in the compound. Sulfur trioxide is SO_3. As you work through the examples, you will get quicker at working out formulae and it will become like a new language to you – the language of Chemistry!

Some formulae have to be learned – such as ammonia (NH_3), water (H_2O), organic compounds like methane (CH_4) and acids such as sulfuric acid (H_2SO_4), hydrochloric acid (HCl), nitric acid (HNO_3).

Remember that ammonia is NH_3 but ammonium is NH_4^+.

Atoms in formulae

Revised

Questions can be asked about the total number of atoms in a given formula or the total number of a specific type of atom.

Example 3
How many atoms are present in one molecule of sulfuric acid, H_2SO_4? There are 2 hydrogen atoms, 1 sulfur atom and 4 oxygen atoms –so there are **7 atoms** in one molecule.

Example 4
How many hydrogen atoms are present in one molecule of $CH_3CH_2CH_2OH$?

The answer is simply the total of all the hydrogen atoms in one molecule – so the answer is **8 atoms**.

Note: *A question could be asked about an unusual molecule – but just add up all the atoms needed.*

Word equations and balanced symbol equations

Revised

● **Word equations** are a long way of representing chemical reactions.

● **Balanced symbol equations** are a more convenient method of doing this.

Equations have to be balanced because no atoms are lost or gained during a chemical reaction – the atoms are just reorganised. There should always be the same number of each type of atom when an equation is balanced.

Exam tip

You may be given an unusual word equation and be asked to write a balanced symbol equation for the reaction. Write the formulae of all the reactants and products, and then balance the equation.

Example 5

Write the balanced symbol equation for the reaction of sodium hydroxide with hydrochloric acid.

1. Write the word equation for the reaction:

   sodium hydroxide(aq) + hydrochloric acid(aq) → sodium chloride(aq) + water(l)

2. Write the formulae of the substances that react together and the substances that are produced.

   Reactants: sodium hydroxide, $NaOH$ (aq), and hydrochloric acid, HCl (aq).

   Products: sodium chloride, $NaCl$ (aq), and water, H_2O (l).

3. Substitute the formulae into the word equation to give you the initial symbol equation:

   $NaOH$ (aq) + HCl (aq) → $NaCl$ (aq) + H_2O (l)

Exam tip

Sometimes, **state symbols** are given to show the physical state of each reactant and each product. The symbols below are used to indicate this:

(aq) means aqueous (dissolved in water); **(l)** means liquid; **(s)** means solid; and **(g)** means gas.

4. It is important to balance all symbol equations so that there are the same numbers of each type of atom on both sides of the equation arrow. In the above equation:

   … you can see that there is the same number of each type of atom on both sides of the equation. This symbol equation is already balanced. So the balanced symbol equation is:

Atoms involved	Reactant side (left-hand side)	Product side (right-hand side)
Na	1	1
O	1	1
H	2	2
Cl	1	1

$NaOH$ (aq) + HCl (aq) → $NaCl$ (aq) + H_2O (l)

Note: *The state symbols are not always necessary and you should only include them when asked to do so in a question. This equation can be written:*

$NaOH$ + HCl → $NaCl$ + H_2O

Exam tip

Be careful to use an arrow and not an equal sign (=) in your equation. This is a chemical equation, not a mathematical one!

Example 6

Write the balanced symbol equation for the reaction of magnesium with hydrochloric acid.

1. Write the word equation for the reaction:

   magnesium + hydrochloric acid → magnesium chloride + hydrogen

2. Write the formulae of the reactants and products.

   Reactants: magnesium, Mg, and hydrochloric acid, HCl.

   Products: magnesium chloride, $MgCl_2$, and hydrogen, H_2.

3. Write the initial symbol equation:

   Mg + HCl → $MgCl_2$ + H_2

   It can be seen clearly that the above symbol equation is not balanced but *it is important to remember that none of the formulae can be changed to balance an equation.*

Atoms involved	Reactant side (left-hand side)	Product side (right-hand side)
Mg	1	1
H	1	2
Cl	1	2

To balance an equation, balancing numbers are written *in front* of specific formulae and the whole formula then becomes multiplied by this number, for example '2HCl' balances the above equation because it gives us 2 H atoms and 2 Cl atoms on the left-hand side. So the balanced symbol equation is:

Mg + $2HCl$ → $MgCl_2$ + H_2

Exam tip

● Balanced symbol equations can be worth 2 or 3 marks. If balancing numbers are needed, there are 3 marks; if balancing numbers are not needed, the equation is worth 2 marks.

Example 7

Write the balanced symbol equation for the reaction of magnesium hydroxide with nitric acid.

1 Write the word equation for the reaction:

magnesium hydroxide + nitric acid → magnesium nitrate + water

2 Put the formulae in the initial symbol equation:

$Mg(OH)_2 + HNO_3 \rightarrow Mg(NO_3)_2 + H_2O$

3 For balancing purposes, the nitrate, NO_3, stays intact (i.e. does not break up) in the reaction and so can be considered as a unit. (If a molecular ion breaks up then its atoms must be considered separately.)

This needs balancing:

● we need 2 'NO_3' on the left-hand side, so '$2HNO_3$' is needed on the left.

● now there are 4 H's on the left-hand side, but only 2 on the right-hand side, so '$2H_2O$' is needed on the right.

● oxygen is now balanced.

So the balanced symbol equation is:

$Mg(OH)_2 + 2HNO_3 \rightarrow Mg(NO_3)_2 + 2H_2O$

Atoms involved	Reactant side (left-hand side)	Product side (right-hand side)
Mg	1	1
O (ignoring the 'O' in nitrate)	2	1
H	3	2
NO_3	1	2

Example 8

Write the balanced symbol equation for the reaction of sodium with water.

1 Write the word equation for the reaction:

sodium + water → sodium hydroxide + hydrogen

2 Put the formulae in the initial symbol equation:

$Na + H_2O \rightarrow NaOH + H_2$

● There are 3 H on the right-hand side and only 2 H on the left, so we need '2NaOH' to give 4 H on right-hand side.

● Then '$2H_2O$' on the left-hand side to make 4 H on both sides.

● Finally '2Na' on the left-hand side to balance the 2 Na now present on the right-hand side.

So the balanced symbol equation is:

$2Na + 2H_2O \rightarrow 2NaOH + H_2$

Exam tip

● Watch hydroxides – many errors occur with calcium hydroxide and copper hydroxide, where the brackets are left out. Calcium hydroxide is $Ca(OH)_2$ and *not* $CaOH_2$.

Atoms involved	Reactant side (left-hand side)	Product side (right-hand side)
Na	1	1
H	2	3
O	1	1

Exam tip

● The most important rule to remember is *never change a formula* to try to balance an equation.

● Also be careful writing formulae – writing 'CL' instead of 'Cl' or 'CA' instead of 'Ca' can lose 2 marks in an equation.

● Remember that diatomic elements, such as oxygen, should *always* be written as 'O_2' in a balanced symbol equation.

● If a substance works out to have '½' as a balancing number, you can multiply all the balancing numbers by 2 to get whole numbers – but you don't have to.

Ionic equations

Some chemical reactions, which involve ionic compounds, are actually reactions between *some* of the ions involved in the mixture. The balanced symbol equation can be rewritten as an **ionic equation** leaving out the ions that do not take part in the reaction.

For each ionic substance in the reaction, write the ions present below it and how many of each ion is present. If an ion appears on both sides of the equation (in the same state), it should not be included in the ionic equation.

Example 10

Write the ionic equation for the reaction between hydrochloric acid and sodium hydroxide.

The balanced symbol equation is shown below along with the particles present:

$HCl + NaOH \rightarrow NaCl + H_2O$

H^+ Na^+ Na^+

Cl^- OH^- Cl^- H_2O

The Na^+ and Cl^- ions are on both sides of the equation, in the same numbers, and so are not part of the ionic reaction. The ionic equation is:

$H^+ + OH^- \rightarrow H_2O$

Ions that do not take part in a reaction are called **spectator ions**.

Example 11

Write the ionic equation for the reaction between copper(II) sulfate solution and sodium hydroxide solution.

The balanced symbol equation is:

$CuSO_4(aq) + 2NaOH\,(aq) \rightarrow Cu(OH)_2(s) + Na_2SO_4\,(aq)$

$Cu^{2+}(aq)$ $2Na^+(aq)$ $Cu^{2+}(OH^-)_2(s)$ $2Na^+(aq)$

$SO_4^{2-}(aq)$ $2OH^-(aq)$ $SO_4^{2-}(aq)$

$2Na^+(aq)$ and $SO_4^{2-}(aq)$ are on both sides of the equation, so are not part of the ionic equation.

The ionic equation is:

$Cu^{2+}(aq) + 2OH^-(aq) \rightarrow Cu(OH)_2(s)$

Example 12

Write the ionic equation for the reaction between potassium chloride solution and silver nitrate solution.

The balanced symbol equation is:

$KCl\,(aq) + AgNO_3\,(aq) \rightarrow AgCl\,(s) + KNO_3\,(aq)$

$K^+(aq)$ $Ag^+(aq)$ $Ag^+Cl^-\,(s)$ $K^+(aq)$

$Cl^-(aq)$ $NO_3^-(aq)$ $NO_3^-(aq)$

$K^+(aq)$ and $NO_3^-(aq)$ are on both sides of the equation, so are not part of the ionic equation.

The ionic equation is:

$Cl^-(aq) + Ag^+\,(aq) \rightarrow AgCl\,(s)$

> ### Exam tip
> Sometimes state symbols have to be included to show exactly which ions have changed and which have not.

> ### Exam tip
> - Writing the incorrect formula for sodium sulfate or sodium carbonate are other common errors. Sodium sulfate is 'Na_2SO_4' and sodium carbonate is 'Na_2CO_3'. Sometimes the small 2 after the sodium gets left out, which loses a mark for the formula and the balancing in the equation.

> ### Exam tip
> - Ionic equations are important in Chapters 6 and 7 and parts of Unit 2.
> - State symbols are most often not required but they may help you to work out which are the spectator ions in a reaction.

1 Write the formulae of these simple compounds:

    a) sodium fluoride; **b)** magnesium oxide; **c)** potassium oxide; **d)** barium chloride.   [4]

2 Write the formulae of these transition metal compounds:

    a) copper(II) chloride; **b)** zinc oxide; **c)** copper sulfate; **d)** iron(III) hydroxide.   [4]

3 Write formulae for: **a)** sodium carbonate; **b)** sodium hydrogen carbonate.   [2]

4 Name the following compounds:

    a) CO_2; **b)** KNO_3; **c)** $CuCO_3$; **d)** HF; **e)** $MgSO_4$.   [5]

5 Write the formulae of these compounds:

    a) ammonium sulfate; **b)** sulfur dioxide; **c)** calcium hydrogen carbonate;
    d) aluminium sulfate.   [4]

6 Sodium thiosulfate has the formula $Na_2S_2O_3$. Write the formula, including the charge, of the thiosulfate ion.   [1]

7 Name the following ions: **a)** OH^-; **b)** O^{2-}; **c)** Cl^-; **d)** Al^{3+}; **e)** SO_4^{2-}.   [5]

8 Write a balanced symbol equation for these reactions:

    a) potassium hydroxide + sulfuric acid → potassium sulfate + water   [3]

    b) calcium + oxygen → calcium oxide   [3]

    c) aluminium + chlorine → aluminium chloride   [3]

9 Write a balanced symbol equation to represent the thermal decomposition of copper(II) carbonate into copper(II) oxide and carbon dioxide.   [2]

10 Ethane (C_2H_6) reacts with oxygen according to the word equation:

    ethane + oxygen → carbon dioxide + water.

    Write a balanced symbol equation for this reaction.   [3]

11 Barium chloride solution reacts with potassium sulfate solution to produce solid barium sulfate and potassium chloride remains in solution.

    a) Write a balanced symbol equation for the reaction.   [3]

    b) Write an ionic equation for the reaction.   [2]

12 Write a balanced symbol equation for these reactions:

    a) calcium hydroxide + hydrochloric acid → calcium chloride + water   [3]

    b) aluminium oxide + sulfuric acid → aluminium sulfate + water   [3]

    c) zinc + hydrochloric acid → zinc chloride + hydrogen   [3]

13 Write a balanced symbol equation for the reaction between nitrogen and hydrogen to produce ammonia.   [3]

14 Write an ionic equation for the reaction between zinc(II) ions and hydroxide ions to produce zinc(II) hydroxide.   [3]

15 Convert the following balanced symbol equations into ionic equations by removing any spectator ions:

    a) $Mg + CuSO_4 \rightarrow MgSO_4 + Cu$ [2]

    b) $Zn + 2HCl \rightarrow ZnCl_2 + H_2$ [3]

    c) $CaCO_3 + 2HCl \rightarrow CaCl_2 + CO_2 + H_2O$ [3]

Go online for the answers   Online

4 The Periodic Table

You need to know the following:

● The **Periodic Table** lists all known elements.

● An **element** is a substance that consists of only one type of atom.

● A **compound** is a substance that consists of two or more elements chemically combined.

● An **atom** is the simplest particle of an element that can exist on its own in a stable environment.

● A **molecule** is a particle that consists of two or more atoms chemically bonded together.

History of development of Periodic Table

Revised

1864 – John Newlands arranged the elements in order of atomic mass and found that the first element was similar to the eighth and the second to the ninth. He called this pattern the **law of octaves**. Newlands' law of octaves was limited in that the noble gases had not yet been discovered, some elements did not fit into the scheme easily (oxygen, sulfur and iron were all in the same group) and Newlands did not have a block of transition metals.

1869 – Dmitri Mendeleev also arranged the elements in order of atomic mass and recognised repeating patterns. However, he left gaps for undiscovered elements and switched the mass order of the elements (for example, iodine and tellurium) to fit the patterns in the table. Using his Periodic Table, Mendeleev was able to predict the properties of undiscovered elements. (The noble gases had still not been discovered).

Features of the modern Periodic Table compared to Mendeleev's Table

Features of modern Periodic Table	Features of Mendeleev's Table
Arranged in order of atomic number More elements (with no gaps) A block of transition metals Noble gases are included Actinides and lanthanides are present	Arranged in order of atomic mass Fewer elements (with some gaps) No block of transition metals Noble gases were not included Actinides and lanthanides were not present

> **Exam tip**
>
> You may be asked for features of Mendeleev's table that are different from the modern Periodic Table. Your answers must relate to Mendeleev's table and not the modern one. You will not gain marks for answers about the modern Periodic Table. Also, if you provide an answer common to both the modern Periodic Table and Mendeleev's table you will not gain marks.

Worked example 1

Describe the work of Mendeleev in the development of the modern Periodic Table. [3]

Answer
● He arranged elements in order of atomic mass. [1]
● He left gaps for undiscovered elements. [1]
● He changed the order of certain elements to suit properties. [1]

> **Exam tip**
>
> The most common mistake is to state that Mendeleev arranged the elements in order of atomic number. Remember that Mendeleev also changed the order of some of the elements, such as iodine and tellurium, to suit their properties better.

Groups and periods

- The **periods** are the horizontal rows of the Periodic Table.
- The **groups** are the vertical columns of the Periodic Table.
- The first period only contains two elements – hydrogen and helium.

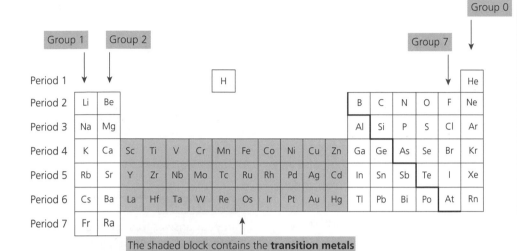

The shaded block contains the **transition metals**

A common question is to name or write the symbol of an element in a certain period and a certain group of the Periodic Table. Remember to count Period 1. For example, chlorine is the element in Period 3 and Group 7. A common mistake is to write bromine – having forgotten to count Period 1.

Metals and non-metals

- The elements to the left of the thick black line in the Periodic Table above are **metals**.
- The elements to the right of the thick black line in the Periodic Table above are **non-metals**.

Exam tip

The thick black line shown on the Periodic Table above divides the metals (left of the line) from the non-metals (on the right). In the exam it is useful to write 'metals' on the left of the Periodic Table and 'non-metals' on the right.

Names of groups

- **Group 1** elements are called the **alkali metals**.
- **Group 2** elements are called the **alkaline earth metals**.
- **Group 7** elements are called the **halogens**.
- **Group 0** (sometimes called **Group 8**) elements are called the **noble gases**.

Exam tip

The names of Group 1 and Group 2 are often confused. Common errors are to call Group 1 the *alkaline* metals and Group 2 the *alkali* earth metals.

Solids, liquids and gases

- Of all the known elements at room temperature and pressure:
  - eleven are gases
  - two are liquids
  - the rest are solids.

- The eleven gases are hydrogen, nitrogen, oxygen, fluorine, chlorine and the noble gases (helium, neon, argon, krypton, xenon and radon)

- The two liquids are bromine (a **non-metal**) and mercury (a **metal**).

- Questions are often asked about changes of state of the elements, and also of some compounds. You must know how to define each change of state, and how to use melting and boiling point data to determine the state of elements and their compounds at specific temperatures.

- **Melting** is the change of state from a solid to a liquid on heating.

- **Boiling** is the change of state from a liquid to a gas on heating.

- **Freezing** is the change of state from a liquid to a solid on cooling.

- **Condensing** is the change of state from a gas to a liquid on cooling.

- **Sublimation** is most often defined as the change of state from a solid directly to a gas on heating – it can also be the change of state from a gas directly to a solid on cooling. Examples of substances that undergo sublimation are carbon dioxide and iodine. Solid carbon dioxide is called 'dry ice'. Iodine changes from a dark grey solid to a purple gas when it is heated.

- The temperature at which a solid changes into a liquid is called its **melting point**. The melting point is also the temperature at which the liquid changes into a solid (freezes).

- The temperature at which a liquid changes into a gas is called its **boiling point.** The boiling point is also the temperature at which the gas changes into a liquid (condenses).

- When a substance melts or freezes the temperature remains constant until the melting or freezes process is completed. The same is true about boiling or condensing at the boiling point.

- **Evaporation** is the change from a liquid to a gas at a temperature below its boiling point. The only melting and boiling points you will be expected to remember are those of water – ice melts at 0 °C and water boils at 100 °C. Temperature is measured in degrees Celsius (°C).

- When a solid substance is heated, the temperature of the solid increases until it reaches its melting point.

- The temperature then remains constant while the substance melts, even though it is still being heated.

- Once all the solid has changed to a liquid, the temperature of the liquid again increases until it reaches its boiling point.

- The temperature remains constant while the substance boils, even though it is still being heated.

- Once all the liquid has changed to a gas the temperature of the gas increases.

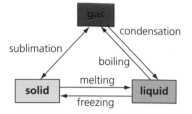

↑ **Changes of state**

Exam tip

In your answer to a question that asks 'What is melting?', you should include both states and whether it is heated or cooled. For example, 'melting is the change of state from *solid* to *liquid* on *heating*'.

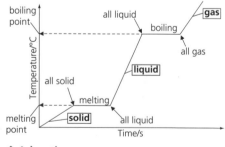

↑ **A heating curve**

Determining state from melting and boiling points

When the melting and boiling points of a substance are given, the state at any temperature can be determined as shown in the examples that follow.

Example 1

Bromine's melting point is −7 °C and its boiling point is 59 °C:

● at temperatures below −7 °C, bromine is a solid

● at temperatures between −7 °C and 59 °C, bromine is a liquid

● at temperatures above 59 °C, bromine is a gas.

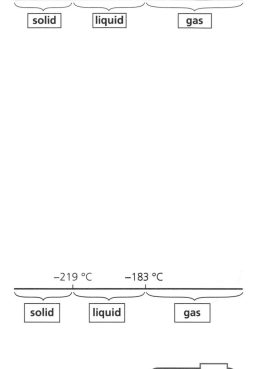

On a temperature line, mark the melting point and the boiling point, with the lowest value (or most negative) furthest to the left:

● at all temperatures *to the left* of (below) the melting point, the substance is a solid

● at all temperatures *between* the melting and boiling points, the substance is a liquid

● at all temperatures *to the right* of (above) the boiling point, the substance is a gas.

Example 2

Oxygen's melting point is −219 °C and its boiling point is −183 °C:

● at −191 °C oxygen is a liquid

● at 45 °C oxygen is a gas

● at −230 °C oxygen is a solid.

Diatomicity

Revised ☐

Some elements exist as **diatomic** molecules.

● 'Diatomic' means that two of the same atoms are bonded together by a covalent bond.

● When writing the formulae of these elements in a balanced symbol equation, they should be written with '$_2$' after the symbol to indicate two atoms joined as a molecule – for example H_2 and O_2.

● There are seven diatomic elements to remember:

hydrogen, H_2; nitrogen, N_2; oxygen, O_2; fluorine, F_2; chlorine, Cl_2; bromine, Br_2 and iodine, I_2.

> **Exam tip**
>
> If asked for the symbol of an element or the symbol for an atom of the element, it is correct to write Cl or H, rather than Cl_2 or H_2.

Properties of the elements

Revised ☐

Similarities among the elements in Group 1

● All are very **reactive metals**.

● All are soft, easily cut metals exposing a shiny surface.

● The shiny surface quickly tarnishes (goes dull) in air.

● All are stored under oil to prevent reaction with oxygen and moisture in the air.

● All react vigorously with water and burn when heated in air.

● All the atoms have one electron in their outer shell.

● All form simple ions with a charge of +; e.g. Na^+, K^+

● All have a valency of 1.

● All have low melting points

● All conduct electricity.

Worked example 2

State the electronic configurations of sodium and potassium atoms and use these to explain what atoms of the two elements have in common. [3]

Exam tip

It is important to state the electronic configurations to gain all the marks in this question.

Answer

Sodium 2,8,1 [1]; potassium 2,8,8,1 [1]

The atoms have 1 electron in their outer shell. [1]

Trends going down Group 1

● The reactivity increases.

● The melting point decreases.

Reactivity of Group 1 elements

All Group 1 elements have similar chemical properties because their atoms have 1 electron in their outer shell.

When the atoms react, they lose this outer shell electron to form an ion. The ion has a full outer shell and is stable. The ion has a single positive charge.

A **half-equation** can be written for the formation of the ion from the atom.

An example using sodium is: $Na \rightarrow Na^+ + e^-$

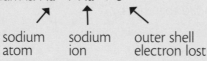

sodium atom   sodium ion   outer shell electron lost

The half-equation for potassium is: $K \rightarrow K^+ + e^-$

Half-equations involve electrons. They are called half-equations because they show only half of the reaction.

Reactions of Group 1 elements with water

The elements of Group 1 react with water to form a metal hydroxide in solution and hydrogen gas. The general equation is:

Group 1 metal + water $\rightarrow$ Group 1 metal hydroxide + hydrogen

For example: sodium + water $\rightarrow$ sodium hydroxide + hydrogen

● Rubidium and caesium are highly reactive and their reactions with water are explosive. These Group 1 elements are not generally used in laboratories but you need to know the products of the reactions, write balanced symbol equations for the reactions and understand why they are not used because of safety.

● When reacting the other elements in the group with water, a small piece of lithium, sodium or potassium is used to ensure that the reaction is controlled. The small piece of the Group 1 element is added to a large trough of water placed behind a safety screen. Gloves and safety goggles should be worn because the Group 1 elements form a corrosive substance on contact with water. The metal element should not be handled directly. Tongs or tweezers can be used to add it to the water.

● Francium is highly radioactive and very rare and so its chemistry is not examined.

Reactions of Group 1 elements with water

Metal	Observations for the reaction with water	Balanced symbol equation
Li	• Floats on the surface • Moves about the surface • Fizzes/gas given off • Eventually disappears • Heat released • Colourless solution formed	$2Li + 2H_2O \rightarrow 2LiOH + H_2$
Na	• Floats on surface • Forms a silvery ball/melts • Moves about the surface • Fizzes/gas given off • Eventually disappears • Heat released • Colourless solution formed	$2Na + 2H_2O \rightarrow 2NaOH + H_2$
K	• Floats on the surface • Moves about the surface • Burns with a lilac flame • Fizzes/gas given off • Eventually disappears • Small explosion/crackle • Heat released • Colourless solution formed	$2K + 2H_2O \rightarrow 2KOH + H_2$

Reactions of Group 1 elements with Group 7 elements

All the Group 1 elements react directly with Group 7 elements.

● The storage of the Group 1 elements under oil along with a surface coating of the oxide may make their reaction with the Group 7 elements slow to start. Adding a drop of water or heating the Group 1 metal can help to start the reaction.

● These reactions form **halides**. A halide can be a fluoride, chloride, bromide or iodide, for example: lithium + iodine → lithium iodide

potassium + chlorine → potassium chloride

● The balanced symbol equations for all the reactions are similar. The general balanced symbol equation can be written as:

$2M + X_2 \rightarrow 2MX$

where M is a Group 1 metal and X_2 is a diatomic Group 7 element. For example:

$2Li + I_2 \rightarrow 2LiI$

$2K + Cl_2 \rightarrow 2KCl$

● The vigour of reaction with a *specific halogen* will depend on the reactivity of the Group 1 element. For example, the reaction of lithium with chlorine is rapid, but the reaction of potassium with chlorine is very vigorous. Again, heating the Group 1 metal or adding a drop of water to the metal can help to start the reaction.

> **Exam tip**
>
> The trend in reactivity in Group 1 can be used to predict how fast and vigorous reactions will be. You may also be given information on the reactions and asked to determine a reactivity series for elements in Group 1. Make sure you can name the products for the reactions of Group 1 elements and also write balanced symbol equations for the reactions.

Similarities between elements in Group 7

- All are **reactive non-metals**.
- All are coloured.
- All exist as diatomic molecules.
- All react with Group 1 elements forming solid, white, ionic compounds.
- All atoms of Group 7 elements have 7 electrons in their outer shell.
- All form simple halide ions with a charge of $-$; for example Cl^- and Br^-.
- All have a valency of 1.
- They do not conduct electricity.
- All the halogens are toxic (See page 60).

Trends going down Group 7

- Colour intensity of the elements darkens and melting point increases.
- The trend in melting point explains why there is clear trend from gas to liquid to solid going down the group.

Iodine gas is purple and the dark grey solid iodine sublimes on heating to form the purple gas when heated. Sublimation is the change of state from solid to gas on heating.

- Based on trends, it would be expected that astatine is a black solid.
- It is hard to compare the toxicity of the halogens because they change from gases to liquids to solid, but in general the toxicity decreases (fluorine is highly toxic even at very low concentrations; iodine can be used as a sterilising agent for wound dressings because it is toxic to bacteria, but not in low concentrations to humans).

- Reactivity decreases – a halogen will displace (from solution) those below it in the group.

Chlorine displacing bromide ions from solution

Observations: The yellow-green gas dissolves in the solution and the solution changes from colourless to red-brown.

Example: chlorine + potassium bromide $\rightarrow$ potassium chloride + bromine

Balanced symbol equation: $Cl_2 + 2KBr \rightarrow 2KCl + Br_2$

Ionic equation: $Cl_2 + 2Br^- \rightarrow 2Cl^- + Br_2$

Chlorine displacing iodide ions from solution

Observations: The yellow-green gas dissolves in the solution and the solution changes from colourless to brown.

Example: chlorine + sodium iodide $\rightarrow$ sodium chloride + iodine

Balanced symbol equation: $Cl_2 + 2NaI \rightarrow 2NaCl + I_2$

Ionic equation: $Cl_2 + 2I^- \rightarrow 2Cl^- + I_2$

Physical properties of Group 7 elements

Group 7 element	Colour and state at room temperature and pressure
Fluorine, F_2	pale yellow gas
Chlorine, Cl_2	yellow-green gas
Bromine, Br_2	red-brown liquid
Iodine, I_2	dark grey solid

Exam tip

Iodine in an aqueous solution of iodide ions is brown.

Bromine displacing iodide ions from solution

Observations: Bromine is red-brown and a solution of iodine in iodide ions is brown, so the solution darkens but it is only a slight change. (However, iodine dissolves in hexane to form a purple solution, so shaking the solution with hexane will change the hexane to a purple colour.)

Example: bromine + magnesium iodide $\rightarrow$ magnesium bromide + iodine

Balanced symbol equation: $Cl_2 + MgI_2 \rightarrow MgCl_2 + I_2$

Ionic equation: $Cl_2 + 2I^- \rightarrow 2Cl^- + I_2$

- It should also be noted that iodine shows no reaction with solutions containing chloride and bromide ions, and that bromine shows no reaction with solution of chloride ions.

- The metal halide used can be any soluble metal chloride, bromide or iodide.

- Fluorine is never used in experiments in school laboratories because it is exceptionally toxic, corrosive, oxidising (see page 60) and it is also difficult to isolate.

- Chlorine water (chlorine dissolved in water) and bromine water are often used in these experiments because they are safer than using the toxic elements and easier to handle. The observations do not include the yellow-green colour of chlorine in these reactions because chlorine water is virtually colourless. Bromine water is red-brown.

- A displacement reaction occurs when a more reactive element becomes an ion and causes a less reactive element to change from an ion to an atom (for the halogens, the atoms formed combine to form a molecule).

> **Exam tip**
>
> The trend in reactivity in Group 7 can be used to predict which displacement reactions will occur. You may also be given information about the reactions and be asked to determine a reactivity series for elements in Group 7.
>
> Make sure you can name the products for the displacement reactions of Group 7 elements, and also write balanced symbol equations and ionic equations for the reactions.

Reactivity of Group 7 elements

All Group 7 elements have similar chemical properties because their atoms have 7 electrons in their outer shell. When the atoms react, they gain one electron to form an ion – the ion has a full outer shell and is stable. The ion has a single negative charge.

A **half-equation** can be written for the formation of the ion from the atom, or from a diatomic molecule of the halogen. The negative ions formed are called halide ions (fluoride, chloride, bromide and iodide).

An example using chlorine is: $Cl + e^- \rightarrow Cl^-$

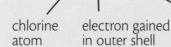

chlorine atom   electron gained in outer shell   chloride ion

A half-equation for iodine is $I + e^- \rightarrow I^-$

The half-equations can also be written for the formation of the ions from a molecule of the diatomic halogen, for example: $Cl_2 + 2e^- \rightarrow 2Cl^-$

Note: *Two electrons are required: one for each of the atoms in Cl_2.*

Remember that half-equations involve electrons. They are called 'half-equations' because they show only half of the reaction.

Note: *In the reaction between sodium and chlorine, each sodium atom loses one electron and each chlorine atom gains one electron. This can be represented by two half-equations:*

$Na \rightarrow Na^+ + e^-$

$Cl + e^- \rightarrow Cl^-$

Similarities between elements in Group 0

Revised

- All are **unreactive non-metals**.
- They are all colourless gases at room temperature.
- All atoms of Group 0 elements have 8 electrons in their outer shell.
- Group 0 elements do not have a valency because they are unreactive having a full outer shell of electrons which makes them stable.

Position in Periodic Table linked to electronic configuration

Revised

The group number of an element is the same as the number of electrons in the outer shell – for example, potassium is in Group 1; there is 1 electron in the outer shell of a potassium atom (see pages 19–20).

Exam tip

The difference in the trend in reactivity of the Group 1 elements compared to the Group 7 elements is often confused. Questions are set which ask for the most reactive element in Group 7. Fluorine is the correct answer. Many students incorrectly state astatine or iodine.

Sometimes an incomplete form of the Periodic Table is given containing only a few of the elements and in the questions that follow you are asked to use *only* the elements given. Many include other elements in their answers that cannot be accepted.

Learn the colour and physical state of the halogens carefully.

Applying trends to unfamiliar elements

Revised

An unfamiliar element is usually one low down in the Periodic Table. Examples of elements commonly used are rubidium, caesium and astatine. Answering questions about these means that you just apply the trends you have learned from those covered above.

1 What are the common names given to:

   a) Group 1; **b)** Group 2; **c)** Group 7; **d)** Group 0?   **[4]**

2 Write a half-equation to represent the formation of a lithium ion from a lithium atom.   **[2]**

3 Which element is in Period 3 and Group 5?   **[1]**

4 Which scientist devised the law of octaves?   **[1]**

5 Give the colour and state at room temperature and pressure of these elements:

   a) fluorine; **b)** chorine; **c)** bromine; **d)** iodine; **(e)** neon.   **[5]**

6 Write the formula of these simple ions:

   a) rubidium; **b)** iodide; **c)** potassium; **d)** fluoride   **[4]**

7 The atoms of an element have the electronic configuration 2,8,6. In which group of the Periodic Table would this element be found?   **[1]**

8 Using only the list of elements below answer these questions:

   sodium   magnesium   oxygen   calcium   fluorine

   iron   carbon   nitrogen   sulfur   bromine

   a) Which **four** of the elements are diatomic?   **[4]**

   b) Name **one** solid non-metal from the list.   **[1]**

   c) Which element would form an ion with a simple charge of +?   **[1]**

   d) Which element is a transition metal?   **[1]**

   e) Which **three** elements are gases?   **[3]**

9 A piece of freshly-cut sodium is shiny but tarnishes in air. What does 'tarnish' mean?   **[1]**

10 Which is the most reactive halogen?   **[1]**

11 What is used to order the elements in the modern Periodic Table?   **[1]**

12 Write a half-equation for the formation of chloride ions from a chlorine molecule.   **[3]**

13 State **three** safety precautions that are required when carrying out the reaction of sodium with water.   **[3]**

14 Write a balanced symbol equation for the following reactions of sodium:

   a) sodium and fluorine   **[3]**

   b) sodium and water.   **[3]**

15 State two features of the Periodic Table developed by Mendeleev that are not present in the modern Periodic Table.   **[2]**

Go online for the answers   Online

5 Quantitative Chemistry

Note: *This section is C1 of GCSE Chemistry and C2 of Double Award Chemistry.*

The atom
Revised

The mass of an atom is largely centred in its nucleus. The **relative atomic mass** (**RAM**) of an atom is measured relative to the mass of an atom of carbon-12 (see page 13). The mass of an atom of carbon-12 is taken to be exactly 12 and the mass of all other atoms are compared to this.

It is important to remember that RAM is an *average* of the mass numbers of all the element's isotopes taking abundance into account. This is why chlorine has a RAM of 35.5 (see page 13).

A **relative formula mass** (**RFM**) is the total of the RAMs of all the atoms present in the formula of a substance.

The mole

Revised

One **mole** of a substance is the standard measurement of amount – 1 mole of any substance contains 6×10^{23} particles. The number of moles of a substance can be determined in various ways, depending on whether it is a solid or in solution.

If you are given a certain mass of a substance, you need to divide the mass in grams by the substance's RFM to calculate the number of moles of the substance:

$$\text{moles} = \frac{\text{mass (g)}}{\text{RFM}}$$

Heating to constant mass

Revised

- When heated, some substances produce gases (including water vapour), which are released to the atmosphere – these substances lose mass on heating.

- When heated, some substances react with gases in the air – these substances gain mass on heating.

- When a solid produces a gas on heating, or reacts with a gas from the air, you should **heat to constant mass** to ensure that the reaction has gone to completion.

- Heating to constant mass means that you heat the substance, allow it to cool and record the mass of the substance – this is repeated until the mass no longer changes.

- The process involves measuring the mass of the empty container, for example a crucible or evaporating basin. The substance is then put in the container and the total mass is measured. The substance is heated in the container and the mass measured on several occasions, after cooling, until there is no further change.

Data involving heating to constant mass may be presented to you as follows:

- mass of crucible   = 21.12 g
- mass of crucible and substance   = 21.60 g
- mass of crucible and contents after heating for 2 minutes   = 21.87 g
- mass of crucible and contents after heating for 4 minutes   = 21.92 g
- mass of crucible and contents after heating for 6 minutes   = 21.92 g

Heating to constant mass has been achieved. This substance gains mass on heating so it is reacting with a gas in the air. The gas in the air that reacts is usually oxygen, though some substances may react with carbon dioxide and even nitrogen.

Mole calculations using these masses can be carried out if you know the RFM of the substance.

Water of crystallisation and degree of hydration

Revised ☐

- **Water of crystallisation** is water that is **chemically bonded** into the **crystal structure**.
- **Hydrated** means that solid crystals contain water of crystallisation.
- **Dehydration** means removal of water of crystallisation.
- An **anhydrous substance** does not contain water of crystallisation.
- The **degree of hydration** is the number of moles of water of crystallisation chemically bonded in 1 mole of the compound. The degree of hydration of hydrated copper(II) sulfate, $CuSO_4.5H_2O$, is 5.
- The '$5H_2O$' in $CuSO_4.5H_2O$ is part of the mass of the solid.
- The degree of hydration of hydrated substances can be determined by heating to constant mass, taking mass measurements before and after or by titration (Unit 2, page 144).
- Hydrated substances can be named in two different ways, for example $BaCl_2.2H_2O$ is called hydrated barium chloride or barium chloride-2-water. The '2' is the degree of hydration. You will need to recognise both.
- Anhydrous barium chloride would have the formula $BaCl_2$ (no water of crystallisation present).

Relative formula mass

Revised ☐

The RFM of a substance can be calculated by adding up all the relative atomic masses (RAMs) of all the atoms in the formula. Relative atomic masses can be found on the Periodic Table in the *Data Leaflet*.

> **Exam tip**
> Make sure you look up relative atomic mass on the *Data Leaflet* and not atomic number.

The term **relative molecular mass** (**RMM**) may sometimes be used. This term is used for compounds, but RFM is most commonly used because it applies to RMM and RAM values. See the following example.

Example 1

What is the RFM of water, H_2O, carbon dioxide, CO_2, lead(II) nitrate, $Pb(NO_3)_2$ and hydrated copper(II) sulfate, $CuSO_4.5H_2O$?

H_2O	contains	2 H atoms	RAM (H) = 1
		1 O atom	RAM (O) = 16

RFM = $(2 \times 1) + 16$ = **18**

CO_2	contains	1 C atom	RAM (C) = 12
		2 O atoms	RAM (O) = 16

RFM = $12 + (2 \times 16)$ = **44**

$Pb(NO_3)_2$	contains	1 Pb atom	RAM (Pb) = 207
		2 N atoms	RAM (N) = 14
		6 O atoms	RAM (O) = 16

RFM = $207 + (2 \times 14) + (6 \times 16)$ = **331**

$CuSO_4.5H_2O$	contains	1 Cu atom	RAM (Cu) = 64
		1 S atom	RAM (S) = 32
		4 O atoms	RAM (O) = 16
		5 H_2O	RFM (H_2O) = 18

RFM = $64 + 32 + (4 \times 16) + (5 \times 18)$ = **250**

> **Exam tip**
> When you calculate RFM values, remember that all the atoms inside brackets are multiplied by the small number outside the bracket.

> **Exam tip**
> When calculating the RFM of hydrated substances that contain water of crystallisation, remember that the degree of hydration tells us that there are a certain number of water molecules in one 'molecule' of the substance. The total RFM of all these water molecules has to be included in the RFM – for example, hydrated nickel(II) sulfate is $NiSO_4.7H_2O$; its RFM is $59 + 32 + (4 \times 16) + (7 \times 18) = 281$.

Interchanging RFM and moles

Revised

The mole expression we used earlier can be written in three ways:

- moles = $\dfrac{\text{mass (g)}}{\text{RFM}}$

- mass (g) = moles × RFM

- RFM = $\dfrac{\text{mass (g)}}{\text{moles}}$

The mass of 1 mole is the RFM in grams

- The RFM of H_2O is 18, so 1 mole of H_2O has a mass of 18 g.
- The RFM of CO_2 is 44, so 1 mole of CO_2 has a mass of 44 g.
- The RFM of $Pb(NO_3)_2$ is 331, so 1 mole of $Pb(NO_3)_2$ has a mass of 331 g.
- The RFM of $CuSO_4.5H_2O$ is 250, so 1 mole of $CuSO_4.5H_2O$ has a mass of 250 g.

This means that we can work through the following calculations:

- 2 moles of water have a mass of 36 g because mass = moles × RFM = $2 \times 18 = 36$
- 0.5 moles of CO_2 have a mass of 22 g because mass = moles × RFM = $0.5 \times 44 = 22$
- 0.01 moles of $Pb(NO_3)_2$ have a mass of 3.31 g because mass = moles × RFM = $0.01 \times 331 = 3.31$
- 0.2 moles of $CuSO_4.5H_2O$ have a mass of 50 g because mass = moles × RFM = $0.2 \times 250 = 50$

... and these to work out how many moles we have:

- 9 g of water is 0.5 moles because moles $= \dfrac{\text{mass (g)}}{\text{RFM}} = \dfrac{9}{18} = 0.5$

- 88 g of carbon dioxide is 2 moles because moles $= \dfrac{\text{mass (g)}}{\text{RFM}} = \dfrac{88}{44} = 2$

- 66.2 g of $Pb(NO_3)_2$ is 0.2 moles because moles $= \dfrac{\text{mass (g)}}{\text{RFM}} = \dfrac{66.2}{331} = 0.2$

- 31.75 g of $CuSO_4.5H_2O$ is 0.127 moles because moles $= \dfrac{\text{mass (g)}}{\text{RFM}} = \dfrac{31.75}{250} = 0.127$

... and to work out the RFM:

- 21 g of an unknown substance contains 0.25 moles, so its RFM is 84

  because RFM $= \dfrac{\text{mass (g)}}{\text{moles}} = \dfrac{21}{0.25} = 84$

The calculation of an RFM can often help to identify a substance or an element in the substance.

Exam tip

Watch out for masses given in kilograms, (kg) (1kg = 1000g) or tonnes (1 tonne = 1000000g). The mass which is divided by the RFM must be in grammes (g).

Exam tip

Answers are normally best given to 2 decimal places for numbers greater than 1 (for example 62.94) and 3 significant figures for numbers less than 1, for example 0.257.

Percentage of water in hydrated compounds

Revised

With hydrated compounds, questions are often set in which the percentage of water of crystallisation by mass is to be calculated. 'By mass' refers to the use of relative atomic masses. This expression calculates the percentage of water in a hydrated compound:

% of water in a compound $= \dfrac{\text{degree of hydration} \times \text{RFM of water}}{\text{RFM of hydrated compound}} \times 100$

Example 2

Find the percentage of water by mass in copper(II) sulfate-5-water, $CuSO_4.5H_2O$.

Formula: $CuSO_4.5H_2O$

RFM $= 64 + 32 + (4 \times 16) + 5 \times (2 + 16) = 250$

Degree of hydration $= 5$

RFM of water $= 18$

% $H_2O = \dfrac{5 \times 18}{250} \times 100 = \textbf{36\%}$

Empirical formula and molecular formula

Revised

The formula that is determined from experimental mass (or percentage) data is called the **empirical formula** – this is the simplest whole number ratio of the combined atoms.

- The molecular formula is the *actual* ratio of the atoms in a compound and this will be a simple multiple of the empirical formula.

- Remember to use the RFM to determine what multiple of the empirical formula you need for a molecular formula.

- Also remember to cancel down the number of each type of atom to the lowest number when determining an empirical formula.

Example 3

The empirical formula of a compound has been determined to be CH_3 and the RFM of the compound is 30. Determine the molecular formula of the compound.

The RFM of CH_3 is $12 + (1 \times 3) = 15$.

So $2 \times CH_3$ must be present in the compound, so its molecular formula is C_2H_6.

Example 4

The empirical formula of a compound is CH_2O, and its RFM is 180. Determine the molecular formula of the compound.

The RFM of CH_2O is $12 + (1 \times 2) + 16 = 30$.

So $6 \times CH_2O$ must be present in the compound, so its molecular formula is $C_6H_{12}O_6$.

Example 5

The molecular formula of a compound is $Na_2S_4O_6$. What is the empirical formula of the compound?

The simplest ratio of the atoms is found by dividing the number of each type of atom by 2 (in this case). Its empirical formula is NaS_2O_3.

Determining formulae of simple compounds

Revised ☐

Simple compounds are formed from just two elements – for example, sodium chloride and magnesium oxide. You can already work out the formula of a simple compound using valency values (See page 31). However, you must also be able to use information about mass to determine the formula of a simple compound.

● You can calculate the numbers of moles of the atoms of each element by dividing the mass of each element by its RAM (always use RAMs for these calculations with elements).

● The moles are then converted to a simple ratio – this is best done by making the lowest mole value = 1 and reducing the others in the same scale. You divide them all by the lowest mole value.

● In some examples, you may be given the masses of the elements that combine; in others you may be given the mass of the compound formed (a simple subtraction will calculate the mass of the second element).

● You also need to be able to plan how to carry out these experiments practically to determine the formula of a simple compound. Most of the experiments involve heating to constant mass but full practical details and apparatus required may be expected.

Example 6

1.06 g of magnesium combines with oxygen to give 1.77 g of magnesium oxide. Find the formula of the oxide of magnesium.

First, work out the mass of oxygen combining with the magnesium using $1.77 - 1.06 = 0.71$ g.

You can then calculate the formula of the oxide of magnesium:

Element	Magnesium	Oxygen
Mass (g)	1.06	0.71
RAM	24	16
Moles	$\frac{1.06}{24} = 0.044$	$\frac{0.71}{16} = 0.044$
Ratio (÷ 0.044)	1	1
Empirical formula	MgO	

Exam tip

Often the masses are given to 2 or 3 decimal places so the moles may not be exactly the same. Use at least three significant figures for the number of moles.

Practical notes

This experiment is carried out as follows:

● Measure the mass of the empty crucible and lid.

● Measure the mass of the lid and crucible containing some magnesium powder.

● Heat the contents of the crucible with the lid on a pipeclay triangle on a tripod over a Bunsen burner

● Raise the lid a little now and again to let more air in.

● Allow the crucible and lid to cool and then measure the mass.

● Heat again and measure the mass again – repeat until the mass is constant.

● The results would not be reliable without these measures in place. Any lack of reliability in the measurements would be because not all of the magnesium reacted, or some product was lost from the crucible.

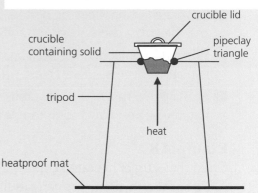

↑ Heating a solid

Exam tip

Powdered magnesium is used because it has a larger surface area, so it reacts more readily.

The sample is heated to constant mass to ensure that all of the magnesium reacts.

Worked example 1

A sample of solid phosphorus was burned in excess oxygen. 0.775 g of phosphorus reacted with 1.0 g of oxygen.

a) Determine the empirical formula of the oxide of phosphorus formed.
[3 marks]

b) Given that the RMM of the oxide of phosphorus is 284, determine the molecular formula of the oxide. [1 mark]

Answer

a)

Element	Phosphorus	Oxygen
Mass (g)	0.775	1.0
RFM	31	16
Moles	$\frac{0.775}{31} = 0.025$ [1]	$\frac{1}{16} = 0.0625$ [1]
Ratio (÷ 0.025)	1	2.5
Multiply by 2 to get whole numbers	2	5
Empirical formula	P_2O_5 [1]	

b) The RFM of $P_2O_5 = (31 \times 2) + (16 \times 5) = 142$; and the RMM of the oxide is 284.

So $2 \times P_2O_5$ must be present in the compound, giving the molecular formula P_4O_{10}. [1]

Determining degree of hydration by heating to constant mass

The method of determining empirical formulae can also be applied to hydrated compounds.

The apparatus used to heat hydrated compounds is shown here.

- If hydrated compounds are heated, they lose water of crystallisation and their mass decreases as the anhydrous compound is formed.
- When the compound has been heated to constant mass, the decrease in mass is the mass of water lost.
- By using the mass of the anhydrous compound and the mass of water lost, the degree of hydration can be determined.

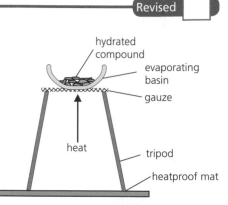

↑ **Apparatus for heating a hydrated compound**

Example 8

Given that 4.0 g of hydrated copper(II) sulfate, $CuSO_4.nH_2O$, produces 2.56 g of the anhydrous copper(II) sulfate $CuSO_4$ on heating to constant mass, find the value of n in the formula of the hydrated salt.

The mass of water lost can be calculated using $4.0 - 2.56 = 1.44$ g.

Compound	Copper(II) sulfate	Water
Formula	$CuSO_4$	H_2O
Mass (g)	2.56	1.44
RFM	$64 + 32 + (16 \times 4) = 160$	$(2 \times 1) + 16 = 18$
Moles	$\frac{2.56}{160} = 0.016$	$\frac{1.44}{18} = 0.08$
Ratio (÷ 0.016)	1	5
Empirical formula	$CuSO_4.5H_2O$	

You can see from the empirical formula that the value of **$n = 5$**.

Example 9

The following mass measurements were taken when a sample of hydrated aluminium nitrate, $Al(NO_3)_3.nH_2O$, was heated to constant mass in an evaporating basin in a low temperature oven.

Mass of evaporating basin = 54.13 g

Mass of evaporating basin and hydrated salt = 61.63 g

Mass of evaporating basin and contents after heating to constant mass = 58.39 g.

Find the degree of hydration in $Al(NO_3)_3.nH_2O$.

Mass of anhydrous salt = 58.39 − 54.13 = 4.26 g

Mass of water lost = 61.63 − 58.39 = 3.24 g

Compound	Aluminium nitrate	Water
Formula	$Al(NO_3)_3$	H_2O
Mass (g)	4.26	3.24
RFM	$27 + (14 \times 3) + (16 \times 9) = 213$	$(1 \times 2) + 16 = 18$
Moles	$\frac{4.26}{213} = 0.02$	$\frac{3.24}{18} = 0.18$
Ratio (÷ 0.02)	1	9
Empirical formula	$Al(NO_3)_3.9H_2O$	

You can see from the empirical formula that the value of **$n = 9$**.

> **Exam tip**
>
> The solid remaining after heating to constant mass is the anhydrous compound. The difference in mass before and after heating is the mass of water lost.

Using balanced symbol equations quantitatively

'Quantitatively' means measuring and calculating quantities.

No atoms are gained or lost in a balanced symbol equation, so the equation can be read quantitatively. This allows mole calculations to be carried out.

A balanced symbol equation such as the one below for the thermal decomposition of lead(II) nitrate can be read **quantitatively**:

$$2Pb(NO_3)_2 \rightarrow 2PbO + 4NO_2 + O_2$$

This equation shows that when 2 moles of $Pb(NO_3)_2$ are heated to constant mass, they break down to produce 2 moles of PbO, 4 moles of NO_2 and 1 mole of O_2.

Remember that the lead(II) nitrate is heated to constant mass to ensure that it all decomposes.

If there is a different number of moles of $Pb(NO_3)_2$ to start with, the balancing numbers in the equation still give the ratio of how many moles react and how many moles of products are made.

There are three steps to follow:

Step 1: Using the mass of one of the reactants, which will be given to you, calculate the number of moles of this substance by dividing by its RFM.

Step 2: Using the balancing numbers in the equation, calculate the number of moles of the substance asked about in the question.

Step 3: Convert the number of moles of this substance to its corresponding mass by multiplying by its RFM.

Worked example 2

$Pb(NO_3)_2$ undergoes thermal decomposition according to the equation:

$$2Pb(NO_3)_2 \rightarrow 2PbO + 4NO_2 + O_2$$

3.31 g of $Pb(NO_3)_2$ were heated to constant mass. Calculate the mass of PbO formed. [5 marks]

Answer
Method 1
a) The RFM of $Pb(NO_3)_2$ = 207 + (14 × 2) + (16 × 6) = 331   [1]

   Moles = $\dfrac{mass}{RFM}$ = $\dfrac{3.31}{331}$ = 0.01 moles of $Pb(NO_3)_2$ [1]

b) In the balanced symbol equation, 2 moles of $Pb(NO_3)_2$ form 2 moles of PbO. So 0.01 moles of $Pb(NO_3)_2$ form 0.01 moles of PbO.   [1]

c) Mass = moles × RFM

   RFM of PbO = 207 + 16 = 223   [1]

   Mass of PbO formed = moles × RFM = 0.01 × 223 = **2.23 g**   [1]

> **Exam tip**
>
> The type of calculation shown in this example is often asked in questions. The most common mistake is to calculate the RFM and then multiply it by the balancing number before calculating the number of moles. *Remember that the RFM is for one formula unit.* The balancing numbers are for that specific equation. In this example, the error would be to use '662' as the RFM of $Pb(NO_3)_2$ because it has a '2' in front of it in the equation.

Method 2

This type of calculation can be set out in a table below the balanced symbol equation.

	2Pb(NO$_3$)$_2$	→	2PbO	+	4NO$_2$	+	O$_2$
Mass	3.31 g		2.23 g***				
RFM	331 [1]		223** [1]				
Moles	0.01 [1]		0.01*				

a) Put in the mass you have been given (3.31 g) and calculate the RFM value of that substance (331). Divide the mass by the RFM to calculate the number of moles (0.01). All this is shown in the column below Pb(NO$_3$)$_2$.

b) Then calculate the other moles using the balancing numbers. 0.01 moles of Pb(NO$_3$)$_2$ produce 0.01 moles of PbO (*).   [1]

c) Calculate the RFM of PbO (**) and multiply it by the number of moles to determine the mass of PbO (***).   [1]

Exam tip

Remember, when using the table method to work down to moles, go across using the balancing numbers and work up to the mass.

Worked example 3

27 kg of aluminium were heated in a stream of oxygen until constant mass was achieved. Determine the mass of aluminium oxide formed.

$4Al + 3O_2 \rightarrow 2Al_2O_3$

Answer
Method 1

a) 27 kg of aluminium is 27 000 g.

$$\text{Moles} = \frac{\text{mass}}{\text{RFM}} = \frac{27\,000}{27} = 1000 \text{ moles of Al.}$$

b) In the balanced symbol equation, 4 moles of Al form 2 moles of Al$_2$O$_3$. So 1000 moles of Al form $\frac{1000}{2} = 500$ moles of Al$_2$O$_3$.

c) RFM of Al$_2$O$_3$ = (2 × 27) + (3 × 16) = 102.

Mass of Al$_2$O$_3$ formed = moles × RFM = 500 × 102
        = 51 000 g = **51 kg**.

Method 2

The table shows step 1 in the first column, step 2 working out other moles*, and step 3 working out RFM** and mass***

	4Al	+	3O$_2$	2Al$_2$O$_3$
Mass	27 000 g			51 000 g ***
RFM	27			102**
Moles	1000			500*

Exam tip

Some questions are set using kilograms so ensure that you know to use mass in grams. *Always* convert to grams before working out moles by dividing a mass by the RFM. This shows the use of scale – particularly when dealing with industrial processes. There will be 1 mark available for converting from the mass unit given to the mass in grams.

Remember that to convert from kilograms to grams you should × 1000; to convert from tonnes to grams you should ×1 000 000.

Worked example 4

7.15 g of hydrated sodium carbonate, Na$_2$CO$_3$.10H$_2$O, were heated in an evaporating basin. Calculate the mass of anhydrous sodium carbonate which remained on heating to constant mass.   [5 marks]

$$Na_2CO_3.10H_2O \rightarrow Na_2CO_3 + 10H_2O$$

Answer
Method 1
a) RFM of hydrated sodium carbonate = $(2 \times 23) + 12 + (3 \times 16)$
   $+ 10 \times (2 + 16) = 286$ [1]

   Moles = $\dfrac{\text{mass}}{\text{RFM}} = \dfrac{7.15}{286} = 0.025$ moles of $Na_2CO_3.10H_2O$.   [1]

b) In the balanced symbol equation, 1 mole $Na_2CO_3.10H_2O$ forms 1 mole of Na_2CO_3

   So 0.025 moles of $Na_2CO_3.10H_2O$ forms 0.025 moles of Na_2CO_3.   [1]

c) RFM of $Na_2CO_3 = (2 \times 23) + 12 + (3 \times 16) = 106$.   [1]

   Mass of Na_2CO_3 formed = moles × RFM = 0.025 × 106 = **2.65 g**.   [1]

Method 2
The table shows step 1 in the first column, step 2 working out other moles* and step 3 working out RFM** and mass***.

	$Na_2CO_3.10H_2O$ →	Na_2CO_3	+	$10H_2O$
Mass	7.15 g	2.65 g*** [1]		
RFM	286 [1]	106** [1]		
Moles	0.025 [1]	0.025* [1]		

Percentage yield   Revised ☐

During a chemical reaction, the calculated number of moles or the calculated mass of the product formed is called the **theoretical yield**. It is the number of moles or mass you would expect to be produced if the reaction went to completion.

● However, many chemical reactions do not give the expected amount of product and the number of moles or the mass you obtain is called the **actual yield**. This is what you obtain experimentally.

● The percentage yield is the percentage of the theoretical yield that is achieved in the reaction. It is calculated using the expression:

   percentage yield = $\dfrac{\text{actual yield}}{\text{theoretical yield}} \times 100$

● The actual yield and theoretical yield may be in moles or as a mass usually in grams, as long as the units are the same.

● The reasons why the percentage yield is not 100% are often asked and the main reasons are:

  ● loss by mechanical transfer (from one container to another)

  ● loss during a separating technique – for example, filtration or using a separating funnel

  ● side-reactions occurring

  ● the reaction not being complete.

Worked example 5

A sample of 3.72 g of copper(II) carbonate was heated in a crucible. The copper(II) carbonate decomposed to give copper(II) oxide and carbon dioxide according to the equation below:

$$CuCO_3 \rightarrow CuO + CO_2$$

a) Calculate the theoretical yield of copper(II) oxide from this reaction. [5 marks]

b) 1.8 g of copper(II) oxide were actually obtained. Calculate the percentage yield of this reaction using your answer to part a. [2 marks]

c) Suggest one reason why the percentage yield was not 100%. [1 marks]

Answer

a)

	$CuCO_3$	$\rightarrow$	CuO	+	CO_2
Mass	3.72 g		$0.03 \times 80 = 2.4\,g$ [1]		
RFM	$64 + 12 + (16 \times 3) = 124$ [1]		$64 + 16 = 80$ [1]		
Moles	$\frac{3.72}{124} = 0.03$ [1]		0.03 [1]		

The theoretical yield is 2.4 g.

b) Percentage yield $= \dfrac{\text{actual yield}}{\text{theoretical yield}} \times 100 = \dfrac{1.8}{2.4} \times 100 = 75\%$ [2]

c) The reaction was not complete. [1]

Revision Questions

1   To what atom are the masses of all atoms compared? [2]

2   Calculate the RFM of these compounds:

   a) H_2SO_4; b) $Ca(OH)_2$; c) $Al_2(SO_4)_3$; d) K_2CO_3; e) $FeCl_3$ [5]

3   Calculate the RFM of these hydrated compounds.

   a) nickel sulfate-7-water; b) $CoCl_2.6H_2O$ [2]

4   Calculate the mass of calcium oxide, CaO, which would be produced by heating a 5 g sample of calcium carbonate, $CaCO_3$, to constant mass.

   $CaCO_3 \rightarrow CaO + CO_2$ [5]

5   What mass of magnesium oxide would be produced when 1.2 g of magnesium powder is burned completely in oxygen?

   $2Mg + O_2 \rightarrow 2MgO$ [5]

6   Aluminium reacts with iron(III) oxide according to the equation:

   $2Al + Fe_2O_3 \rightarrow Al_2O_3 + 2Fe$

   Calculate the mass of iron(III) oxide required to react with 54 kg of aluminium. [5]

7   What mass of iron would be produced in the reaction in question 6? [3]

8   100 g of an oxide of iron contains 27.6 g of oxygen. Determine the empirical formula of the oxide. [3]

9 Calculate the percentage of water of crystallisation in these hydrated compounds:

   a) copper(II) chloride-2-water   **[3]**

   b) $Na_2CO_3 . 10H_2O$ **[3]**

10 3.2 g of copper turnings are heated in air. The copper reacts with oxygen to form 4.0 g of an oxide of copper. Determine the empirical formula of the oxide of copper.   **[4]**

11 A compound has the empirical formula HO. Its RFM is 34. Determine the molecular formula of the compound.   **[1]**

12 Which one of these represents an empirical formulae?   **[1]**

    $C_2H_4O_2$ $C_{18}H_{36}O_2$ CH_2O

13 A sample of 1.55 g of phosphorus was heated in chlorine to form solid phosphorus(V) chloride, PCl_5. The phosphorus reacts according to the equation:

    $2P + 5Cl_2 \rightarrow 2PCl_5$ **[1]**

   a) Calculate the theoretical yield of phosphorus(V) chloride.   **[5]**

   b) 8.34 g of phosphorus(V) chloride were obtained. Calculate the percentage yield using your answer to part **a**.   **[2]**

   c) Suggest one reason why the percentage yield was not 100%.   **[1]**

14 A compound of sulfur was found to contain 40 g of sulfur and 60 g of oxygen. Determine the empirical formula of the compound.   **[3]**

15 A sample of hydrated sodium carbonate, $Na_2CO_3 . nH_2O$, was heated to constant mass in an evaporating basin. The measurements below were taken at 5-minute intervals:

mass of evaporating basin	= 122.400 g
mass of evaporating basin and hydrated sample	= 122.900 g
mass of evaporating basin and sample after 5 minutes heating	= 122.714 g
mass of evaporating basin and sample after 10 minutes heating	= 122.612 g
mass of evaporating basin and sample after 15 minutes heating	= 122.612 g

   a) Calculate the mass of anhydrous sodium carbonate present at the end of the experiment.   **[2]**

   b) Calculate the number of moles of anhydrous sodium carbonate present at the end of the experiment.   **[2]**

   c) Calculate the mass of water lost by heating.   **[2]**

   d) Calculate the number of moles of water lost by heating.   **[2]**

   e) Using your answer to parts **b** and **d**, determine the value of n in $Na_2CO_3 . nH_2O$.   **[2]**

Go online for the answers   Online

6 Acids, Bases and Salts

Hazard symbols
Revised

Hazard symbols are displayed on bottles of chemicals, including acids and alkalis and some salts.

Hazard symbols are used rather than words because they are immediately recognisable and there are no language issues with symbols – they are recognised worldwide.

- Toxic chemicals represent a serious risk of causing death by poisoning.
- Corrosive chemicals can burn and destroy living tissue.
- Explosive chemicals may explode if heated, exposed to a flame or knocked.
- Flammable chemicals, in contact with air, may catch fire easily.
- The caution hazard symbol indicates that the chemical may cause an allergic skin reaction.

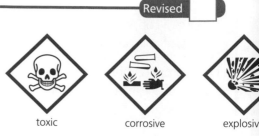

toxic   corrosive   explosiv

flammable   caution

↑ **Hazard symbols**

Risk assessment
Revised

Any risk to an individual should be minimised by having safety procedures in place to avoid any hazard when using chemicals.

For example:

- with corrosive substances, personal protective equipment (safety glasses, gloves and lab coat) should be worn.
- with toxic substances, contact with the substance should be minimised by using personal protective equipment and they should be used in a fume cupboard if appropriate.
- with flammable substances, there should be no naked flames in the laboratory.
- with substances labelled 'caution,' care should be taken in handling to avoid spills and personal protective equipment should be worn.

Exam tip

When carrying out a risk assessment always consider the hazards associated with the reactants and products of a chemical reaction.

Indicators
Revised

An **indicator** is a chemical that gives a **colour change** in acidic, alkaline and neutral solutions.

- Some indicators are solutions (e.g. phenolphthalein) but some commonly used ones are also available in paper form for ease of use (e.g. red and blue litmus and universal indicator).
- The paper form of universal indicator is often simply called 'pH paper'.
- Indicator papers are most often used by placing them on a white tile and using a glass rod to put a drop of the solution being tested on the paper.
- Gases can be tested using damp indicator paper held in the gas.

Indicators commonly used are litmus and phenolphthalein. The colours of these in acidic, alkaline and neutral solution are given in the table on the next page.

Indicator colours

Indicator	Colour in acid solution	Colour in neutral solution	Colour in alkaline solution
Phenolphthalein	Colourless	Colourless	Pink
Red litmus	Red	Red	Blue
Blue litmus	Red	Blue	Blue

To determine whether a substance is acidic or alkaline, both litmus indicators may need to be used:

● If a solution is added to blue litmus and it remains blue, it could be a neutral solution or an alkaline solution.

● Red litmus would need to be used to confirm if the soultion was neutral or an alkali – red litmus changes to blue if the solution is an alkali and stays red if it is a neutral solution.

pH
Revised

A **pH** (always written lower case 'p' and capital 'H') value is a numerical value used to indicate how acidic or alkaline a solution is.

● It is a scale that runs from 0 to 14:

  ● a pH of 7 is neutral

  ● a pH value less than 7 is acidic

  ● a pH value more than 7 is alkaline.

Universal indicator can be used to measure the pH of a solution.

● A few drops of universal indicator are added to the solution being tested and the colour observed. The pH is determined by comparing the colour to a pH colour chart.

● If the paper indicator is used, a few drops of the solution are dropped onto the paper – again the observed colour is compared to a pH colour chart.

The table below gives the expected colours with universal indicator for strong acids, weak acids, neutral solutions, weak alkalis and strong alkalis. Common examples are also given.

Exam tip

A common question is to describe how to determine the pH of a solution. You need to use universal indicator solution or pH paper, and observe the colour obtained. You determine the pH by comparing the colour obtained to a colour chart.

The pH scale

pH	0	1	2	3	4	5	6	7	8	9	10	11	12	13	14
Colour	Red			Orange		Yellow		Green		Green-blue	Blue		Purple		
Strength	Strong acid			Weak acid				Neutral	Weak alkali				Strong alkali		
Examples	Hydrochloric acid Sulfuric acid Nitric acid			Ethanoic acid Carbonic acid				Water	Ammonia				Sodium hydroxide Potassium hydroxide		
Common solutions	Gastric juice			Vinegar Lemon juice				Salt solution	Blood Seawater				Oven cleaner		

A pH meter is an electronic device that gives a numerical value of pH, often to 1 or 2 decimal places – e.g. the pH of dilute ethanoic acid is 3.22. This would make ethanoic acid a weak acid because the pH is greater than 2 but less than 7.

Validity and reliability

- Validity is part of the overall design of the experiment.
- Reliability depends on whether or not the same result could be obtained again if the experiment were to be repeated.
- Red litmus can identify a substance as alkaline, but it stays red for both neutral substances and acids. Blue litmus can identify a substance as acidic, but stays blue with both neutral substances and alkalis. Both red and blue litmus should be used to identify a substance as neutral – using just red litmus to identify a neutral solution would not be a valid experiment.
- Universal indicator can identify a substance as acidic, alkaline or neutral, but also whether it is a weak or strong acid or alkali, and give an approximate pH value based on the scale on a colour chart.
- An experiment to determine the pH of a solution using red and blue litmus would not be valid because red and blue litmus would not give enough information to determine pH, unless the solution is neutral.
- A pH meter gives the most detailed information because it gives a numerical value for pH to 1 or 2 decimal places – so a solution with a pH of 3.4 would be orange with universal indicator, but there would be no clear indication of where exactly it would be in the 3–4 pH range. A pH meter solves this problem.
- The results of these experiments would be reliable because they are able to be reproduced.

Formulae of acids and alkalis

Revised

Acids

Hydrochloric acid is $\mathbf{H}Cl$; sulfuric acid is $\mathbf{H_2}SO_4$; ethanoic acid is $CH_3COO\mathbf{H}$; carbonic acid is $\mathbf{H_2}CO_3$; nitric acid is $\mathbf{H}NO_3$

- All acids contain hydrogen atoms.
- Some or all of these hydrogen atoms are 'acidic' (shown in bold above).
- The acidic hydrogen atoms can ionise in water to form hydrogen ions.
- If the acid ionises completely in water, the acid is a **strong acid**.
- If the acid ionises partially in water, the acid is a **weak acid**.

Alkalis

Ammonia is NH_3; sodium hydroxide is $NaOH$; potassium hydroxide is KOH.

- All alkalis contain, or can produce, hydroxide ions in water.
- Some alkalis contain hydroxide ions and when they dissolve in water the hydroxide ions are released into the solution.
- Ammonia reacts with water to produce hydroxide ions:

  $NH_3 + H_2O \rightarrow NH_4^+ + OH^-$
- If an alkali ionises completely in water, the alkali is a **strong alkali**.
- If an alkali ionises partially in water, the alkali is a **weak alkali**.

Ions in acids and alkalis

Revised

- All acids dissolve in water producing hydrogen ions in solution, H^+(aq).
- All alkalis dissolve in water producing hydroxide ions in solution, OH^-(aq).
- **Neutralisation** is the reaction between an acid and an alkali producing a salt and water only. It can be represented by the general equation:

  acid + alkali $\rightarrow$ salt + water

- The equation for neutralisation can be written as an ionic equation:

  H^+(aq) + OH^-(aq) $\rightarrow$ H_2O (l)

> **Exam tip**
>
> The ionic equation for neutralisation is common in questions and the most common mistake is to leave out the state symbols.

Bases and alkalis

Revised

A **base** is a substance that reacts with an acid producing a salt and water.

- Common bases are metal oxides and metal hydroxides. Copper(II) oxide, CuO; magnesium oxide, MgO; potassium hydroxide, KOH and sodium hydroxide, NaOH, are all bases because they are metal oxides and hydroxides.
- An **alkali** is a soluble base.
- The most common alkalis are sodium hydroxide, NaOH; potassium hydroxide, KOH; calcium hydroxide, $Ca(OH)_2$; and ammonia, NH_3.
- Ammonia is not a metal oxide or hydroxide but a solution of ammonia in water contains hydroxide ions, OH^-, so it is an alkali.

> **Exam tip**
>
> Check the back of the *Data Leaflet* for solubility information. The majority of oxides and hydroxides are insoluble in water, so most are 'just' bases and only a few can be called alkalis. Don't forget that ammonia is an alkali.

Reactions of acids

Revised

Acids produce salts when they react.

- A salt is a compound formed when the hydrogen ions in an acid are replaced with metal ions (or ammonium ions).
- Acids are solutions containing hydrogen ions, H^+, and a negative ion.
- The negative ion (anion) is what combines with a metal ion to form the salt.
- Hydrochloric acid, HCl, contains hydrogen ions, H^+, and **chloride** ions, Cl^-. So when hydrochloric acid reacts, it forms a **chloride**.
- Sulfuric acid, H_2SO_4, contains hydrogen ions, H^+, and **sulfate** ions, SO_4^{2-}. So when sulfuric acid reacts, it forms a **sulfate**.
- Ethanoic acid, CH_3COOH, contains hydrogen ions, H^+, and **ethanoate** ions, CH_3COO^-. When ethanoic acid reacts, it forms an **ethanoate**.
- Nitric acid, HNO_3, contains hydrogen ions, H^+, and **nitrate** ions, NO_3^-. So when nitric acid reacts, it forms a **nitrate**.

You can remove the H^+ ions from the acid molecule to work out the formula of the anion – for every H^+ you remove, give the anion one more negative charge.

> **Note:** *The reactions of nitric acid, potassium hydroxide, ammonia and all metal hydrogen carbonates are not required in Double Award Chemistry.*

The reactions of acids can be summarised as follows.

1 Acids + metals

Dilute acids react with some metals to produce a salt and hydrogen gas. The general word equation is:

metal + acid → salt + hydrogen

Examples are:

● magnesium + hydrochloric acid → magnesium chloride + hydrogen

$Mg + 2HCl \rightarrow MgCl_2 + H_2$

● zinc + sulfuric acid → zinc sulfate + hydrogen

$Zn + H_2SO_4 \rightarrow ZnSO_4 + H_2$

The hydrogen produced in these reactions can be tested by applying a lit splint to the top of the test tube – if hydrogen is present a pop sound is heard. The pop is caused by the hydrogen burning explosively in air. It reacts with oxygen to produce water:

$2H_2 + O_2 \rightarrow 2H_2O$

> **Exam tip**
>
> Don't forget that hydrogen is diatomic. Also, remember that acids do not react with copper or any other metal below copper in the reactivity series.

2 Acids + metal oxides/hydroxides

Dilute acids react with metal oxides and metal hydroxides to produce a salt and water. Metal oxides and hydroxides are bases. The general word equations are:

metal oxide + acid → salt + water

metal hydroxide + acid → salt + water

Examples are:

● copper(II) oxide + sulfuric acid → copper sulfate + water

$CuO + H_2SO_4 \rightarrow CuSO_4 + H_2O$

● sodium hydroxide + hydrochloric acid → sodium chloride + water

$NaOH + HCl \rightarrow NaCl + H_2O$

3 Acids + metal carbonate/hydrogen carbonate

Dilute acids react with metal carbonates and metal hydrogen carbonates to produce a salt, carbon dioxide and water. Only Group 1 elements form stable solid hydrogen carbonates. Group 2 hydrogen carbonates can exist in solution but not as solids. The general word equations are:

metal carbonate + acid → salt + carbon dioxide + water

metal hydrogen carbonate + acid → salt + carbon dioxide + water

Examples are:
● copper(II) carbonate + sulfuric acid → copper(II) sulfate + carbon dioxide + water

$CuCO_3 + H_2SO_4 \rightarrow CuSO_4 + CO_2 + H_2O$

● potassium hydrogen carbonate + nitric acid → potassium nitrate + carbon dioxide + water

$KHCO_3 + HNO_3 \rightarrow KNO_3 + CO_2 + H_2O$

The carbon dioxide produced in these reactions can be tested by bubbling the gas through limewater (calcium hydroxide solution) using a delivery tube.

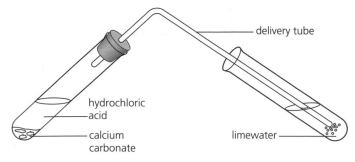

delivery tube

hydrochloric acid

calcium carbonate

limewater

↑ **Testing for carbon dioxide**

If carbon dioxide is present, the limewater changes from colourless to milky.

4 Acids + ammonia

Dilute acids react with ammonia to form an ammonium salt only. The general word equation is:

ammonia + acid → ammonium salt

Examples are:

- ammonia + hydrochloric acid → ammonium chloride

  $NH_3 + HCl \rightarrow NH_4Cl$

- ammonia + sulfuric acid → ammonium sulfate

  $2NH_3 + H_2SO_4 \rightarrow (NH_4)_2SO_4$

Concentration of solutions
Revised

Concentration is measured in **moles per dm³** (mol/dm^3) – so the concentration of a solution is the number of moles of a solute dissolved in $1\,dm^3$ of solution. The solvent is usually water.

- $2\,mol/dm^3$ hydrochloric acid is twice as concentrated as $1\,mol/dm^3$ hydrochloric acid.

- $2\,mol/dm^3$ hydrochloric acid has 2 moles of HCl dissolved in $1\,dm^3$ of the solution.

In this unit you only need to be aware that these are the units in which concentration is measured.

Observations during acid reactions
Revised

- If a solid metal or metal compound reacts with an excess of acid, the solid will disappear.

- Many acid reactions are exothermic – so the observation 'heat is released' applies to most reactions of acids.

- For metals that react with acids, and metal carbonates and metal hydrogen carbonates reacting with acids, a gas is produced – so the observation 'bubbles of a gas produced' applies.

- All acids are colourless solutions so you can work out if the colour of the solution changes during an acid reaction. For example:

magnesium + hydrochloric acid → magnesium chloride + hydrogen

  - hydrochloric acid is a colourless solution

  - magnesium chloride is a salt and is soluble in water (*Data Leaflet*)

  - magnesium compounds are colourless in solution, so magnesium chloride solution is colourless

  - there is no change to the colour of the solution.

  Observations: The solution remains colourless; bubbles of gas are produced; the magnesium disappears; heat is released.

- Another example:

copper carbonate + sulfuric acid → copper sulfate + water + carbon dioxide

  - sulfuric acid is colourless

  - copper sulfate is soluble in water (*Data Leaflet*)

  - and is blue in solution.

  Observations: The solution changes from colourless to blue; bubbles of gas are produced; the copper carbonate disappears; heat is released.

Exam tip

All Group 1 and 2, ammonium, aluminium and zinc compounds are white solids. If they dissolve in water they form colourless solutions. (When zinc oxide is heated it turns yellow, but it changes back to white on cooling.)

Exam tip

Copper(II) compounds vary in colour – copper(II) oxide is black; copper(II) carbonate is green; hydrated copper(II) sulfate is blue; anhydrous copper(II) sulfate is white; all copper(II) compounds that dissolve in water form blue solutions.

Temperature changes in a reaction

 Revised

- Most reactions of acids are exothermic (release heat) – in an exothermic reaction the temperature of the reacting solution increases.

- A few reactions of acids are endothermic (take in heat) – in an endothermic reaction the temperature of the reacting solution decreases.

The temperature of an acid reaction can be followed using a thermometer or a temperature probe linked to a computer. With a thermometer, usually the initial temperature and the highest temperature reached are recorded.

A temperature probe linked to a computer will produce a graph of temperature against time, and the maximum temperature or temperature increase can be determined from the graph. Small temperature changes are difficult to measure with a standard thermometer so the more sensitive temperature probe is preferred, or a narrow range thermometer.

The reaction should be carried out in an insulated container such as a polystyrene cup to avoid heat exchange with the surroundings.

- The graph shows the results of using a temperature probe with 25 cm³ of 1 mol/dm³ sulfuric acid reacting with 0.5 g of magnesium ribbon. The initial and highest temperature recorded can be found from the graph – they are 21 °C and 31 °C respectively. The reaction is exothermic as the temperature increases.

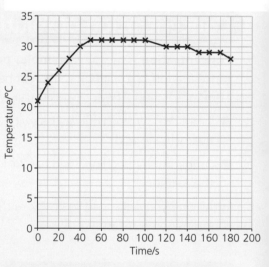
↑ The temperature change during a neutralisation reaction

When preparing a pure, dry sample of a salt there are two different methods. Which method is best depends on the solubility of the substance which reacts with the acid.

The acid chosen depends on the anion in the salt:

● if the salt is a chloride, hydrochloric acid is used

● if the salt is a sulfate, sulfuric acid is used

● if the salt is a nitrate, nitric acid is used

● if the salt is an ethanoate, ethanoic acid is used.

Both methods involve **preparation** and then **purification**.

Method 1: Titration

This method is used for making all sodium and potassium salts – the alkali used is either sodium hydroxide solution or potassium hydroxide solution.

The titration is carried out using a **pipette** to measure an exact volume of one solution; the other solution is added from a **burette**.

Both solutions are colourless, so an indicator, such as phenolphthalein, is used to indicate when the reaction is complete.

Preparation: Pipette 25.0 cm³ of the alkali into a conical flask and add a few drops of phenolphthalein indicator, which gives a pink colour. Fill the burette to the mark with the acid and run it into the conical flask until the colour changes to colourless. Record the volume of acid used. Repeat without the indicator using the same volumes to get a pure, neutral solution of the salt.

Instead of repeating without indicator, the indicator can be removed by adding charcoal, heating and filtering the solution. The charcoal absorbs the indicator.

Purification: Heat the solution to evaporate water from it – reduce the volume by half and leave it to cool and crystallise. Then filter off the crystals and dry them between two sheets of filter paper (or in a low temperature oven or in a desiccator).

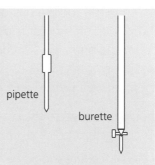
pipette
burette

↑ **Apparatus for titration**

> **Exam tip**
>
> In purification, the salt solution is not heated to dryness because the crystals may contain water of crystallisation. The crystals are allowed to form slowly in solution. Often questions state that you are trying to form pure, dry crystals of hydrated salts (e.g. hydrated copper(II) sulfate, $CuSO_4.5H_2O$) so always heat to reduce the volume by half and allow to cool and crystallise.

Method 2: Using an insoluble solid

This method uses an insoluble solid (a base or a carbonate) containing the metal ion. Using a metal carbonate has an advantage because when it reacts it produces a gas (CO_2) – so when all the acid has been neutralised, no more bubbles will be produced.

The solid used to neutralise the acid is added bit by bit to the acid and will eventually be in excess – some of it will lie unreacted at the bottom of the reaction vessel. It may be necessary to warm the acid.

Preparation: Add excess of the insoluble solid to 25 cm³ of acid in a conical flask. Heat and stir and make sure that there is some unreacted solid left. Then filter off the insoluble solid (**residue**) and pour the filtered liquid (**filtrate**) into an evaporating basin (page 7).

Purification: Heat to evaporate water from it – reduce the volume by half and leave it to cool and crystallise. Then filter off the crystals and dry them between two sheets of filter paper (or in a low temperature oven or in a desiccator).

> **Exam tip**
>
> The methods of drying crystals are often asked about and there are three, as mentioned above. You need to know all three because you may be given one or two of them and be asked for another suitable method for drying the crystals – it is not acceptable to leave them on a window ledge or dry them using paper towels.

Planning a salt preparation

If you are asked to describe a method for the preparation of a salt, you first need to choose the method.

For the preparation of sodium and potassium salts, use the titration method with the pipette and burette:

● The solution chosen is sodium hydroxide or potassium hydroxide. $25.0\,cm^3$ of this solution should be pipetted into a conical flask and 3–5 drops of phenolphthalein added. The solution changes to pink.

● The acid chosen depends on the anion in the required salt (for a chloride you use hydrochloric acid, etc.)

● The acid should be added to the conical flask from a burette. The soultion will change from pink to colourless.

● The rest of the procedure should be followed according to method 1 above.

For the preparation of all other soluble salts use the insoluble solid method:

● The acid chosen depends on the anion in the salt (for a sulfate use sulfuric acid, etc.)

● A suitable volume, e.g. $25\,cm^3$, of the acid should be poured into a conical flask.

● The insoluble solid could be a metal, metal oxide, metal hydroxide, metal carbonate or metal hydrogen carbonate – these all provide the cation in the required salt.

● Excess of the chosen insoluble solid is added to the acid.

● The rest of the procedure should be followed according to method 2 on page 67.

1 What is an alkali? [2]

2 Name two **compounds** that would react with sulfuric acid to make a solution of copper(II) sulfate. [2]

3 Plan an experiment to prepare pure, dry crystals of hydrated sodium sulfate from sodium hydroxide solution and dilute sulfuric acid. [8]

4 State the colour of universal indicator paper and the approximate pH of these solutions:

a) sodium hydroxide; **b)** hydrochloric acid; **c)** ammonia; **d)** ethanoic acid; **e)** water [10]

5 Write the formula of the ion that is present in all acids. [1]

6 Name two bases. [2]

7 Explain the meaning of the following hazard symbols, and what safety precautions should be in place when using a chemical with each symbol displayed on it. [6]

a)   **b)**   **c)**

8 Write an ionic equation for neutralisation, including state symbols. [3]

9 State the colours observed when phenolphthalein is added to:

a) hydrochloric acid; **b)** water; **c)** sodium hydroxide solution [3]

10 Write balanced symbol equations for each of these reactions of acids:

a) magnesium + hydrochloric acid [3]

b) magnesium hydroxide + hydrochloric acid [3]

c) calcium carbonate + hydrochloric acid. [3]

11 State what you would observe in these reactions:

a) zinc and hydrochloric acid [3]

b) copper(II) carbonate and sulfuric acid. [3]

12 Name the salt produced when sodium hydroxide reacts with hydrochloric acid. [1]

13 Using a pH meter, a solution is found to have a pH of 3.8. State what colours you would expect to observe if this solution was tested with these indicator papers:

a) red litmus; **b)** blue litmus; **c)** universal indicator; **d)** phenolphthalein [4]

14 What gas is produced when zinc reacts with dilute sulfuric acid. How would you test for this gas? [3]

15 Copper(II) carbonate is added in excess to dilute hydrochloric acid. The excess copper(II) carbonate is filtered off and the filtered solution is heated to reduce the volume of water. On cooling, crystals are obtained.

a) What is the general name given to the solid removed by filtration? [1]

b) What is the general name given to the filtered solution? [1]

c) Explain how the crystals are removed from the solution and dried. [2]

d) Draw a labelled diagram of the assembled apparatus used to carry out the filtration. [3]

Go online for the answers   Online

7 Tests for Ions

This section deals with the identification of the positive ions and negative ions in an ionic compound. It is important to be able to:

- determine the ions present, given the observations for the tests
- state the observations given a named ionic compound
- describe in detail how to carry out the tests for ions
- evaluate the validity of the evidence provided.

Basic information   Revised

Remember that the positive ion in an ionic compound is called the cation; the negative ion is called the anion.

A flame test can be used to identify some cations. All the other cation and anion tests depend on the formation of a **precipitate**. Precipitate can be abbreviated to 'ppt' when writing results.

- A precipitate is a solid that can be formed on mixing two solutions.
- The substance being investigated is dissolved in water (or dilute nitric acid if it does not dissolve in water). A few cm^3 of this solution are placed into a test tube.
- At first a few drops of the second solution are added, and then a larger volume – this is done to see if the precipitate redissolves in excess of the second solution – this is carried out with the tests for cations.
- The formation of a precipitate, its colour and sometimes whether or not the precipitate redissolves in excess of the second solution are the important factors in identifying the ion present.

You must be able to state the chemical name of any precipitate as well as write a balanced symbol equation and an ionic equation for its formation.

Cation tests   Revised

Cations can be tested for in two different ways – using a flame test and using sodium hydroxide solution.

Flame test

A flame test is carried out like this.

- Dip a flame test rod in deionised water.
- Place the rod in a non-luminous Bunsen flame to clean it.
- Put the flame test rod in the sample.
- Heat the sample in a non-luminous Bunsen flame.
- Observe the colour of the flame.

Note: *A piece of nichrome wire can be used instead of a flame test rod. If nichrome wire is used it should be dipped in concentrated hydrochloric acid before putting it in the sample.*

> **Exam tip**
> If you are asked to describe how to carry out a flame test to identify a specific ion, remember to state the flame test colour you would expect.

Many potassium compounds are contaminated with sodium compounds so it is difficult to see the lilac colour of the potassium ion because the sodium ion gives a strong golden yellow colour. Holding the sample at the edge of the flame can help in seeing the lilac colour.

Metal chlorides are usually used for flame tests (or the chloride can be made by adding a little concentrated hydrochloric acid to the solid) because the chloride ion will not affect the flame test colour in any way.

Results: The table shows the results for the flame test of the ions you need to know.

Colour	Ion present
Golden yellow	Na^+
Lilac	K^+
Brick red	Ca^{2+}
Apple green	Ba^{2+}
Blue-green	Cu^{2+}

Exam tip

Remember that you need to be able to identify an ion from the flame colour, and also to state the flame colour from the named ion present.

Sodium hydroxide solution

This method of identification of cations relies on the production of distinctive precipitates.

● Add a few drops of sodium hydroxide solution to the test solution containing the cation.

● Note your observations.

● Continue to add the sodium hydroxide solution until it is in excess.

● The colour of precipitate and whether or not it redissolves in excess sodium hydroxide solution identifies the cation present.

Exam tip

In evaluating these tests, if more than a few drops of sodium hydroxide solution are added initially in the Al^{3+} and Zn^{2+} tests, no precipitate may be observed because it could already have dissolved.

Also Al^{3+} and Zn^{2+} give the same results (a white precipitate, which is soluble in excess sodium hydroxide forming a colourless solution). This test is not conclusive for these ions. Another test using aqueous ammonia will be used in Unit C2 that will distinguish between them.

Cation test observations using sodium hydroxide solution

Cation present	Colour of precipitate	Solubility in excess sodium hydroxide solution
Mg^{2+}	White	Insoluble/does not redissolve
Cu^{2+}	Blue	Insoluble/does not redissolve
Al^{3+}	White	Soluble/redissolves forming a colourless solution
Fe^{2+}	Pale green	Insoluble/does not redissolve
Fe^{3+}	Red-brown	Insoluble/does not redissolve
Zn^{2+}	White	Soluble/redissolves forming a colourless solution

Equations for precipitation reactions

You need to be able to write balanced symbol equations and ionic equations for these precipitation reactions.

1. You will be told the names of the reactants that are in solution. Write the formulae for these and then draw an equation arrow.

2. Identify the precipitate – in these examples it will be an insoluble hydroxide, for example magnesium hydroxide is the white precipitate in the first test in the table.

3. Write the formula of the precipitate as one of the products.

4. Whatever ions are left over from the reactants remain in solution as the other product – combine these ions to find the formula of the second product.

5. Write the balanced symbol equation.

Exam tip

There is solubility information in the *Data Leaflet* that will help you to identify a possible insoluble compound that will form as a precipitate.

Example 1

A few drops of sodium hydroxide solution are added to magnesium chloride solution. A white precipitate is observed. Write a balanced symbol equation for the reaction.

1. *Reactants*: magnesium chloride ($MgCl_2$) and sodium hydroxide (NaOH)

2. *Precipitate*: magnesium hydroxide

3. *Formula*: $Mg(OH)_2$

4. *Ions left over*: Na^+ and Cl^-, so sodium chloride is the other product (NaCl)

5. *Balanced symbol equation*: $MgCl_2 + 2NaOH \rightarrow Mg(OH)_2 + 2NaCl$

Exam tip

The number of marks awarded to the equation will tell you if you need to use balancing numbers. A 2 mark equation does not require balancing numbers if all the formulae are written correctly. A 3 mark equation will require balancing numbers.

Writing an ionic equation for a precipitation reaction

1. Identify the precipitate.

2. Write the formula for the precipitate – this will be the only product.

3. Identify the two ions that are part of the precipitate – these will be the two reactants.

4. Write the equation and balance it if more than one of the ions is required.

Exam tip

Check the *Data Leaflet* to ensure that the compound you have chosen as the precipitate is insoluble.

Example 2

Write an ionic equation for the reaction between copper(II) sulfate solution and sodium hydroxide solution.

1. *Precipitate*: copper(II) hydroxide

2. *Formula*: $Cu(OH)_2$

3. *Ions used*: Cu^{2+} and OH^-

4. *Ionic equation*: $Cu^{2+} + 2OH^- \rightarrow Cu(OH)_2$

Note: *There are two hydroxide ions in $Cu(OH)_2$ so you need to put a balancing number of 2 in front of the OH^- on the left hand side.*

Exam tip

This equation is worth 3 marks – one for the Cu^{2+} and OH^- on the left-hand side; one for the $Cu(OH)_2$ on the right; and one for the balancing number.

All the ionic equations for the precipitation reactions with sodium hydroxide solution are given below – but note that unfamiliar ones can be asked for reactions that are not on the course. The reactants and products will be given.

- Aluminium ion: $Al^{3+} + 3OH^- \rightarrow Al(OH)_3$
    white precipitate
- Magnesium ion: $Mg^{2+} + 2OH^- \rightarrow Mg(OH)_2$
    white precipitate
- Copper(II) ion: $Cu^{2+} + 2OH^- \rightarrow Cu(OH)_2$
    blue precipitate
- Iron(II) ion: $Fe^{2+} + 2OH^- \rightarrow Fe(OH)_2$
    pale green precipitate
- Iron(III) ion: $Fe^{3+} + 3OH^- \rightarrow Fe(OH)_3$
    red-brown precipitate
- Zinc ion: $Zn^{2+} + 2OH^- \rightarrow Zn(OH)_2$
    white precipitate

Anion tests
Revised

The anion present in compounds can be tested for by making a solution of the compound in water. If it doesn't dissolve in water, dissolve it in some dilute nitric acid.

- Pour a few cm^3 of the solution into a test tube, and add a few cm^3 of the second solution listed in the table below. You may observe the formation of a precipitate.

- The formation of a precipitate and its colour are important in identifying the anion present in the original compound.

Anion tests observations

Anion	Second solution	Result
Chloride, Cl$^-$	Silver nitrate solution	White precipitate
Bromide, Br$^-$	Silver nitrate solution	Cream precipitate
Iodide, I$^-$	Silver nitrate solution	Yellow precipitate
Sulfate, SO_4^{2-}	Barium chloride solution	White precipitate

Exam tip

Again, a question can ask for a balanced symbol equation or an ionic equation for all the precipitation reactions.

Example 3
The addition of silver nitrate solution to a solution of sodium bromide produces a cream precipitate of silver bromide (AgBr).

The balanced symbol equation for this reaction is:

$AgNO_3 + NaBr \rightarrow AgBr + NaNO_3$

The ionic equation for the reaction is:

$Ag^+ + Br^- \rightarrow AgBr$

Planning an experiment

You may be asked a question about planning an experiment to determine the ions present in a given compound. Remember to:

- describe how to carry out the test
- state the results you would expect based on the ions present in the compound.

Exam tip

Don't forget to dissolve the sample in water before adding either sodium hydroxide **solution** or silver nitrate **solution** or barium chloride **solution**. The word 'solution' is often left out and can cost you a mark.

Revision Questions

1 What would be observed when a solution of silver nitrate is added to a solution containing potassium iodide? [2]

2 Describe how to carry out a flame test on a sample of sodium chloride, and the observations you would make. [4]

3 Name the precipitates formed in these reactions:

  a) sodium hydroxide solution and iron(III) chloride solution [1]

  b) barium chloride solution and magnesium sulfate solution [1]

  c) sodium hydroxide solution and zinc nitrate solution. [1]

4 Write balanced symbol equations for the reactions in question 3.

  a) [3]; **b)** [2]; **c)** [3]

5 Write ionic equations for the reactions in question 3.

  a) [3]; **b)** [2]; **c)** [3]

6 What would be observed in each of the reactions in question 3? [3]

7 An unknown ionic compound was dissolved in water. A sample was placed in a test tube and sodium hydroxide solution was added. A white precipitate was observed, which did not dissolve in excess sodium hydroxide solution. To another sample of the solution, silver nitrate solution was added and a yellow precipitate was observed.

  a) Write the formula of the cation present in the compound. [1]

  b) Write the formula of the anion present in the compound. [1]

  c) Name the unknown ionic compound [1]

8 Write an ionic equation for the reaction of silver nitrate solution with sodium chloride solution. [2]

9 Name one ion that would give a pale green precipitate when sodium hydroxide solution is added to a solution containing the ion. [1]

10 What is meant by the term 'precipitate'? [2]

Go online for the answers

Online

8 Solubility

Water as a solvent
Revised

Water is a common solvent – many substances dissolve in it.

● A **solvent** is a liquid in which a solute dissolves.

● A **solute** is a solid that dissolves in a solvent.

● A **solution** is a mixture of a dissolved solute and a solvent.

● **Soluble** describes a substance that dissolves.

● **Insoluble** describes a substance that does not dissolve.

● A **saturated solution** is one in which the maximum amount of solute has dissolved in the solvent *at a particular temperature*.

> **Exam tip**
>
> The physical properties of water and the test for water using anhydrous copper(II) sulfate (page 90) are required for Double Award Chemistry C1.

Making a solution

The method used to make a solution is shown here.

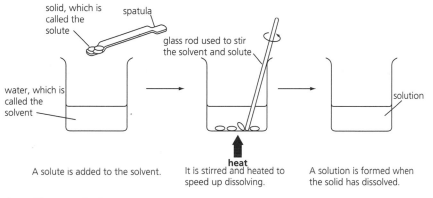

↑ Making a solution

Making a saturated solution

The method used to make a saturated solution is shown here.

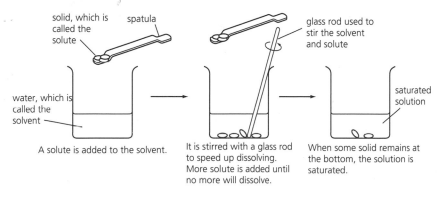

↑ Making a saturated solution

The excess solid remaining at the bottom can be removed by filtration (see page 7).

> **Exam tip**
>
> A glass rod should be used to stir – do not stir with a spatula. Spatulas used for stirring may contaminate other chemicals, and sometimes a metal spatula may react with a solution.

General rules for solubility

Revised

Ionic compounds are *mostly* soluble in water. The *Data Leaflet* gives information on which substances are soluble and which are insoluble. The general rules for solubility of ionic compounds are:

- All nitrates are soluble in water.
- Most sulfates and chlorides are soluble in water, but there are a few exceptions.
- Most oxides, hydroxides and carbonates are insoluble in water, but there are a few exceptions.
- All sodium, potassium and ammonium compounds are soluble in water.

Covalent substances are *mostly* insoluble in water, but there are exceptions such as the gases ammonia, hydrogen chloride and sulfur dioxide as well as solid substances like sugar. Giant covalent substances such as diamond and graphite are insoluble in water.

Look back at pages 26–29 to make sure you can decide on the type of structure of a substance.

> **Exam tip**
>
> You may be given information on the solubility of different substances in water and be asked to state the general rules for solubility of covalent and ionic substances, or among a range of ionic substances.

Making a solid dissolve more quickly

Revised

To make a solid dissolve more quickly several things can be done:

- *Stirring*: a solid dissolves faster in a solvent if it is stirred.
- *Adding more solvent*: a solid dissolves faster if there is more solvent.
- *Heating*: a solid dissolves faster if the temperature of the solvent is increased.
- *Making the solid particles smaller*: a solid dissolves faster if it is crushed into a fine powder. The solid can be crushed in a mortar using a pestle.

↑ **Pestle and mortar**

Solubility

Revised

Solubility is the mass of solute that will saturate 100 g of water (or solvent) at a particular temperature – the units of solubility are **g/100 g of water**.

Another way of saying this is that solubility is the maximum mass of a solute that can dissolve in 100 g of water at a particular temperature.

> **Exam tip**
>
> The most common mistake in this question is to miss the term 'mass' and use 'amount', which is incorrect. This is a very common question and you should learn the definition of solubility thoroughly.

Worked example 1

What is meant by the term 'solubility'?   [4]

Answer

The mass [1] of solute which saturates [1] 100 g of water [1] at a particular temperature [1]

Some solubility values

- Potassium chlorate(V), $KClO_3$, has a solubility of 14 g/100 g water at 40 °C.
- Potassium chloride, KCl, has a solubility of 40 g /100 g water at 40 °C.

> **Note:** *This means that 14 g of potassium chlorate(V) is required to saturate 100 g of water at 40 °C*

More on units of solubility

The units of solubility are important when you are working with graphs and for understanding calculations.

● Mass is measured in g (grams)

Volume is measured in cm^3 (cubic centimetres)

$1 cm^3 = 1$ ml (millilitre)

Water has a density of $1 g/cm^3$

$1 cm^3$ of water has a mass of $1 g$

$1 g$ of water has a volume of $1 cm^3$

$100 g$ of water is the same as $100 cm^3$ of water.

● The values for the solubility of most **gases** in water are low, so the units are usually mg/l (milligrams per litre). 1 mg is $\frac{1}{1000}$ th of a gram.

1 litre $= 1000$ ml $= 1000 cm^3$.

Preparing a salt
Revised

Once a solution of a salt has been prepared, it is often **crystallised** (see page 67).

This process involves heating to evaporate some water (usually until half the volume of water is removed). The solution is then left to cool and crystallise – crystallisation happens because the solubility of a salt *decreases* as the solution cools,

The table shows the change in solubility of potassium chloride (a typical solid) with temperature – as the temperature increases, the solubility of potassium chloride increases.

Temperature (°C)	0	10	20	30	40	50	60	70	80	90	100
Solubility (g/100 g water)	28	31	34.5	37.5	40	43	45.5	48.5	51	54	56.5

Solubility of gases
Revised

● Oxygen, carbon dioxide and hydrogen are not very soluble in water. These gases are collected over water.

● Hydrogen chloride, sulfur dioxide and ammonia are very soluble in water. These gases cannot be collected over water (see pages 114–115).

Thermal pollution

Water is used as a coolant in many factories. As the water cools the factory machinery, it becomes warmer and runs out into rivers and lakes. The temperature of the water in the lakes and rivers increases. The solubility of oxygen *decreases* at a higher temperature. This leads to fish dying due to lack of oxygen.

Worked example 2

Explain why many dead fish were found in a river into which a power station released large amounts of hot water. [3]

Answer

The solubility of oxygen [1] decreases as the temperature increases [1]; so fish die from lack of oxygen [1].

Practical method of determining solubility

Revised

You need to be able to plan an experiment that will allow you to determine a solubility value. This is the most common practical procedure used. The following steps are shown in the diagram below:

1 Weigh a clean, dry boiling tube.

2 Add some solid (see step 7) and reweigh the boiling tube.

3 Add 10 cm³ of deionised water to the boiling tube from a pipette (a burette can be used). Using a pipette is an accurate way of measuring a volume of a liquid. Liquids are drawn up (sucked up) into the pipette using a pipette filler.

4 Put a thermometer in the boiling tube.

5 Heat the boiling tube in a water bath until all the crystals dissolve. Stir gently using the thermometer.

6 Allow the solution to cool slowly (while still stirring) and record the temperature when crystals appear.

7 For the most commonly used solids, between 1 and 5 g of the solid is placed in 10 g of water. If no crystallisation was observed in step 6, try again with more solid – and if the solid didn't all dissolve on heating then use less solid and try again.

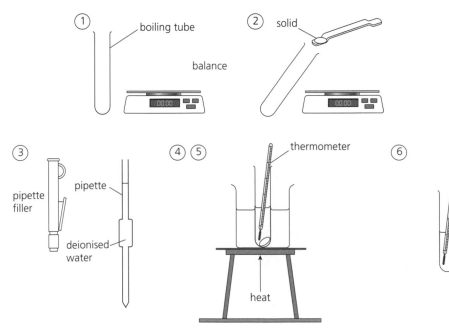

↑ **Determining the solubility of a solid**

Calculating solubility values

The data obtained from solubility experiments is usually the mass of solid, the mass of water and the temperature. These are the three pieces of information required to calculate a solubility value.

Example 1

10 g of sodium chloride was added to 10 g of water at 20 °C. The solution was stirred. The solution was filtered, and the residue was dried and weighed; 6.4 g of residue remained. Calculate the solubility of sodium chloride at 20 °C.

Mass of sodium chloride needed to saturate 10 g of water =
10 − 6.4 = 3.6 g

Solubility at 20 °C = 3.6 × 10 = **36 g/100 g of water**.

Example 2

3.1 g of potassium chlorate(V) were stirred in 10 cm³ (10 g) of water in a boiling tube and heated in a water bath until all the solid dissolved. The solution was allowed to cool and crystals formed at 71 °C. Determine the solubility of potassium chlorate(V) at 71 °C.

Mass of potassium chlorate(V) that saturates 10 g of water at 71 °C = 3.1 g

Solubility of potassium chlorate(V) at 71 °C = 3.1 × 10 = **31 g/100 g water**.

Note: *It is practically difficult to maintain a sample of water at a particular temperature and also to determine the exact mass required to saturate the water. Example 1 above is not a common method, whereas Example 2 is used extensively.*

Water of crystallisation

Some of these terms were met on page 49:

- **water of crystallisation** is water that is chemically bonded into a crystal structure.
- **hydrated** means that solid crystals contain water of crystallisation.
- **dehydration** means removal of water of crystallisation – this can be carried out by heating or by using a chemical dehydrating agent.
- **anhydrous** means without water of crystallisation.

Drawing and using solubility graphs

Solubility values can be plotted against temperature and a curve (or line) is drawn. The x-axis is temperature (°C) and the y-axis is solubility (g/100 g water).

Worked example 3

Draw a solubility curve for potassium chlorate(V), $KClO_3$, using the data shown in the table.

Temperature (°C)	0	10	20	30	40	50	60	70	80	90	100
Solubility of $KClO_3$ (g/100 g water)	3	5	7.5	10.5	14	19	24	30	38	46	54

Answer   [4 marks]

The values in the table were plotted on a graph. [3] for correct plotting of points; [1] for best fit curve.

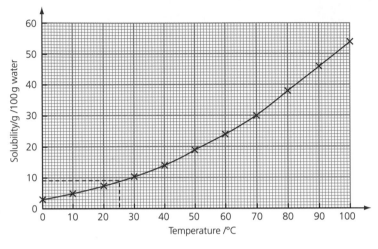

↑ A solubility curve

Determining solubility at intermediate values

Example 3

From the solubility graph for $KClO_3$, what is the solubility of potassium chlorate(V) at 25 °C?

On the graph, a vertical line is drawn from the required temperature up to the solubility curve. A second line is drawn horizontally to the solubility axis to determine the solubility at this temperature.

The solubility of potassium chlorate(V) at 25 °C is **9 g/100 g water**.

Determining the mass of crystals formed on cooling a saturated solution

When a saturated solution cools down, the solubility of a solid *decreases* as the temperature *decreases*.

The difference between the solubility values at two different temperatures is the mass of solid formed on cooling a saturated solution containing 100 g of water.

Example 4

Using the $KClO_3$ solubility graph, determine the mass of solid formed on cooling a saturated solution containing 100 g of water from 75 °C to 25 °C.

The solubility of potassium chlorate(V) at 75 °C = 34 g/100 g water; and its solubility at 25 °C = 9 g/100 g water

When a saturated solution containing 100 g of water is cooled form 75 °C to 25 °C the mass of solid that crystallises is 34 − 9 = **25 g**.

Exam tip

- You may be asked to plot a solubility curve using given data, and then to use your graph to answer further questions. Or you may be given a curve and asked to use it to carry out solubility calculations.

- Plot points using crosses, ×, with the centre of the cross at the exact coordinate.

- The solubility at 0 °C is *not* 0 g/100 g water, so do not plot (0, 0) on a solubility curve.

- Draw the best-fit curve or line on the graph through the crosses – a curve is usually more suitable than a line.

- The graph allows you to determine solubility values at temperatures between the given values.

Note: *Determining the mass of solid that crystallises when the mass of water is not 100 g in the saturated solution is a common question (see Example 5).*

Example 5

If a saturated solution of potassium chorate(V) containing 50 g of water is cooled from 75 °C to 25 °C what is the mass of solid crystals formed?

Solubility at 75 °C = 34 g/100 g water

Solubility at 25 °C = 9 g/100 g water

When a saturated solution containing 100 g of water is cooled from 75 °C to 25 °C the mass of solid that crystallises is 34 − 9 = 25 g.

When a saturated solution containing 50 g of water is cooled from 75 °C to 25 °C the mass of solid that crystallises $\frac{25}{2}$ = **12.5 g**.

Note: *If the mass of water is greater than 100 g, the difference in solubility values will need to be multplied – for example, with 500 g of water, the difference in solubility values will be multiplied by 5.*

Worked example 4

The solubility values of potassium nitrate are given in the table.

Temperature (°C)	0	10	20	30	40	50	60
Solubility of potassium nitrate (g/100 g water)	28	30.5	33	36	39	42	45

1 Determine the mass of potassium nitrate that would be obtained on cooling a saturated solution containing 1000 g of water from 60 °C to 20 °C. [4]

2 A solution was prepared by mixing 15 g of potassium nitrate with 50 g of water at 30 °C. Determine whether or not the solution is saturated. [1]

Answers

1 The solubility at 60 °C is 45 g/100 g water; the solubility at 20 °C is 33 g/100 g water.

For a solution with 100 g of water, the mass of crystals obtained = 45 − 33 [1] = 12 g [1]

For a solution with 1000 g of water, the mass of crystals obtained = 12 × 10 [1] = **120 g** [1]

2 The solubility of potassium nitrate at 30 °C = 36 g/100 g water.

The maximum mass of potassium nitrate that can dissolve in 50 g of water = $\frac{36}{2}$ = 18 g.

So a solution containing 15 g of potassium nitrate in 50 g of water is **not saturated**.

(3 g more of potassium nitrate could be dissolved to make the solution saturated.)

> **Exam tip**
>
> The most common mistake in this type of question is to leave out the last step, where you convert to the mass of water given in the question. Always check the question to make sure you have taken this into account. The marks are usually for subtraction of the solubility values at the two temperatures, and then either division or multiplication depending on the mass of water present.
>
> (*Don't* subtract the temperature values.)

1 State how the solubility of a gas changes as the temperature is increased.   [1]

2 What is meant by these terms:

    a) solvent; **b)** solute; **c)** solution; **d)** saturated solution?   [4]

3 What is water of crystallisation?   [2]

4 What are the units of solubility?   [1]

5 This is the solubility curve of potassium nitrate:

    a) Determine the solubility of potassium nitrate at 25 °C.   [1]

    b) 20 g of potassium nitrate were added to 50 g of water at 20 °C. Is the solution formed saturated? Explain your answer.   [2]

    c) What mass of potassium nitrate would saturate a solution containing 200 g of water at 33 °C?   [2]

    d) What mass of potassium nitrate would crystallise from solution when a saturated solution containing 50 g of water is cooled from 43 °C to 23 °C?   [4]

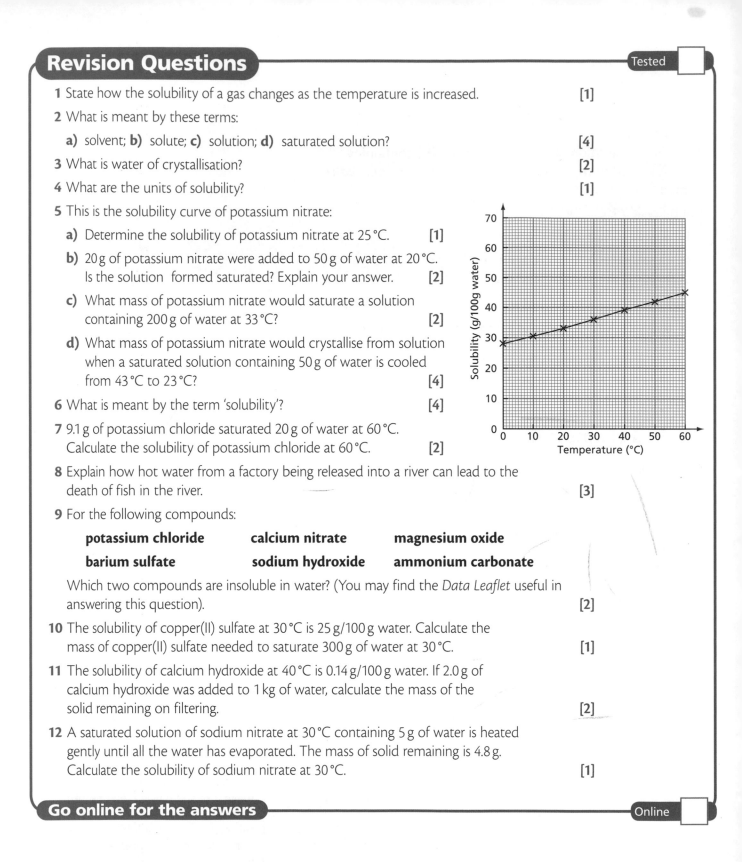

6 What is meant by the term 'solubility'?   [4]

7 9.1 g of potassium chloride saturated 20 g of water at 60 °C. Calculate the solubility of potassium chloride at 60 °C.   [2]

8 Explain how hot water from a factory being released into a river can lead to the death of fish in the river.   [3]

9 For the following compounds:

    potassium chloride   **calcium nitrate**   **magnesium oxide**

    barium sulfate   **sodium hydroxide**   **ammonium carbonate**

    Which two compounds are insoluble in water? (You may find the *Data Leaflet* useful in answering this question).   [2]

10 The solubility of copper(II) sulfate at 30 °C is 25 g/100 g water. Calculate the mass of copper(II) sulfate needed to saturate 300 g of water at 30 °C.   [1]

11 The solubility of calcium hydroxide at 40 °C is 0.14 g/100 g water. If 2.0 g of calcium hydroxide was added to 1 kg of water, calculate the mass of the solid remaining on filtering.   [2]

12 A saturated solution of sodium nitrate at 30 °C containing 5 g of water is heated gently until all the water has evaporated. The mass of solid remaining is 4.8 g. Calculate the solubility of sodium nitrate at 30 °C.   [1]

Go online for the answers   Online

9 Reactivity Series of Metals

The reactivity series of metals (page 88) predicts the vigour of reactions of metals with:

- air (oxygen)
- water – including steam.

Reactions of metals with air (oxygen) Revised

When metals react with air they gain mass because they form an oxide. The table summarises the reactions of common metals with oxygen from the air.

Reactions of some metals with air/oxygen

Metal	Reaction when heated in air	Reaction with air under normal conditions	Balanced symbol equation and notes
K	Burns with lilac flame forming a white solid	When freshly cut the shiny surface tarnishes (goes dull) quickly	$4K + O_2 \rightarrow 2K_2O$
Na	Burns with a golden yellow flame forming a white solid		$4Na + O_2 \rightarrow 2Na_2O$
Ca	Burns with red flame forming a white solid	React slowly forming an oxide layer on the surface	$2Ca + O_2 \rightarrow 2CaO$
Mg	Burns with a bright, white light forming a white solid		$2Mg + O_2 \rightarrow 2MgO$
Al	Burns only when finely powdered, forming a white solid		$4Al + 3O_2 \rightarrow 2Al_2O_3$
Zn	Burns steadily forming a yellow solid, which becomes white on cooling		$2Zn + O_2 \rightarrow 2ZnO$
Fe	Burns with orange sparks when in the form of filings, forming a black solid		$3Fe + 2O_2 \rightarrow Fe_3O_4$ Fe_3O_4 is a mixed oxide
Cu	Does not burn but forms a black solid		$2Cu + O_2 \rightarrow 2CuO$

Sodium, potassium and calcium are only heated in air under very careful supervision and strict safety procedures. The reactions can be extremely dangerous.

All the other metals listed in the table can be heated in air in a crucible using the apparatus shown in the diagram.

Usually the powder form of the metal is heated. The crucible lid is lifted occasionally during heating to allow more air to get into the crucible.

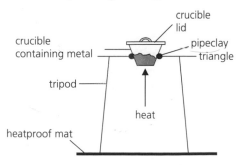

crucible lid

crucible containing metal

pipeclay triangle

tripod

heat

heatproof mat

↑ **Reacting metals with air**

Reaction of metals with water

When sodium and potassium are reacted with water, a small piece of the metal is placed in a trough half-full of water. This reaction is carried out behind a safety screen. Tongs or tweezers are used to handle the metal.

The table summarises the reactions of some of the more reactive metals with water.

Reactions of some metals with water

Metal	Reaction with water	Balanced symbol equation and notes
K	• Floats on the surface • Moves around the surface • Burns with a lilac flame • Fizzes giving off a gas • Heat is released • Small explosion/crackles • Eventually disappears • Forms a colourless solution	$2K + 2H_2O \rightarrow 2KOH + H_2$ Potassium is stored under oil to prevent it reacting with oxygen and moisture in the air
Na	• Floats on the surface • Melts and forms a silvery ball • Fizzes giving off a gas • Heat is released • Eventually disappears • Forms a colourless solution	$2Na + 2H_2O \rightarrow 2NaOH + H_2$ Sodium is stored under oil to prevent it reacting with oxygen and moisture in the air
Ca	• Fizzes giving off a gas • Sinks then rises • Heat is released • Eventually disappears • Forms a colourless solution	$Ca + 2H_2O \rightarrow Ca(OH)_2 + H_2$
Mg	• A very slow reaction • A few bubbles of gas given off	$Mg + 2H_2O \rightarrow Mg(OH)_2 + H_2$

To react calcium or magnesium with water, the metal is put in water in a beaker and an inverted filter funnel is placed over the metal. A boiling tube filled with water is used to collect the hydrogen produced. The apparatus is shown here.

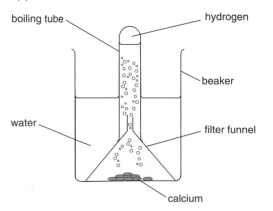

↑ **Reacting metals (not Group 1) with cold water**

When magnesium is used instead of calcium, only a few bubbles of gas are produced over a period of several days.

Reaction of metals with steam

The table summarises the reactions of some metals with steam.

Reactions of some metals with steam

Metal	Reaction with steam	Balanced symbol equation
Mg	• The heated ribbon burns with a bright, white light • Forms a white solid • Heat is released	$Mg + H_2O \rightarrow MgO + H_2$
Al	• No reaction in foil form, unless the protective layer of aluminium oxide is removed • Powdered form burns to form a white solid • Heat is released	$2Al + 3H_2O \rightarrow Al_2O_3 + 3H_2$
Zn	• Powdered form glows to form a yellow solid, which changes to white on cooling • Heat is released	$Zn + H_2O \rightarrow ZnO + H_2$
Fe	• Powdered form glows at red heat forming a black solid	$3Fe + 4H_2O \rightarrow Fe_3O_4 + 4H_2$

Exam tip

Copper (and metals below it in the reactivity series) do not react with water or steam.

The apparatus below is used to allow steam to react with a heated metal. The apparatus is connected to a delivery tube and the gas produced is collected over water using a beehive shelf and a gas jar. The gas produced is hydrogen.

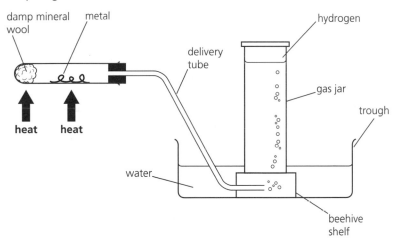

↑ **Reacting a metal with steam**

Damp mineral wool is heated to generate steam. When the heating stops, there is a risk of 'suck back' occurring (the water in the trough being drawn back into the hot boiling tube). This can be prevented by removing the apparatus from the water in the trough or taking the bung out of the boiling tube.

Exam tip

When drawing a diagram, remember that marks are awarded for the labels on an assembled and recognisable diagram – for example, you will *not* gain a mark for a beaker labelled as a crucible. Make the apparatus look like it should. The most common mistakes made when drawing the apparatus to react metals with steam is to put the delivery tube through the wall of the trough. Remember that the level of the water in the trough should always be above the beehive shelf.

Displacement reactions

A **displacement reaction** is one in which a **more reactive metal** forms ions and causes a **less reactive metal ion** to change to atoms – this process involves the transfer of electrons, see pages 100–102.

There are two main types of displacement reaction:

● a solid metal reacting with a solution of a metal ion

● a solid metal reacting with a solid metal oxide.

> **Exam tip**
>
> You may be asked for balanced symbol equations, ionic equations and observations for these reactions. You may be asked to use information to determine a reactivity series.

Solutions

The main observations to look out for are:

● any colour changes in the solution – copper(II) sulfate solution is frequently used because it gives a definite colour change

● the release of heat because displacement reactions are exothermic – more heat will be released the bigger the difference in the reactivity of the metals

● the solid metal which is displaced from solution appearing – remember to state its colour and the fact that a solid is produced.

Worked example 1

Magnesium metal reacts when placed in a solution of copper(II) sulfate.

a) State the observations for the reaction. [3]

b) Write a balanced symbol equation for the reaction. [2]

c) Identify an ion that does not take part in the reaction (spectator ion). [1]

d) Write an ionic equation for the reaction. [2]

> **Exam tip**
>
> Questions may be set using an unusual reaction and you will need to use your knowledge of the colours of reactants and products to predict observations. Write down as many sensible observations as you can for the reaction – even if there are only 2 marks because sometimes observations are combined in mark schemes.

Answers

a) Blue [1] solution fades/changes to colourless [1];
a red-pink/black [1] solid [1] appears;
heat is released [1] [max. 3]

b) $Mg + CuSO_4 \rightarrow MgSO_4 + Cu$ [2]

c) The sulfate ion/SO_4^{2-} (does not take part in the reaction and is the same in both reactants and products) [1]

d) $Mg + Cu^{2+} \rightarrow Mg^{2+} + Cu$ [2]

> **Exam tip**
>
> A maximum of 3 out of the 5 marks available is awarded for the observations. The ionic equation is worked out by removing the spectator ion or ions from the balanced symbol equation.

Determining the reactivity of a metal

Revised

Displacement reactions can be used to determine a reactivity series.

- A set of reactions between metals and their metal salt solutions is carried out.
- The metals are placed in a solution of the metal salt (usually the sulfate or nitrate because most sulfates are soluble in water and all nitrates are soluble in water). The results are recorded in a table like the one shown.

Displacement reactions

Metal salt solution / Metal	Magnesium sulfate	Copper(II) sulfate	Iron(II) sulfate	Zinc sulfate
Magnesium	░░░	✓	✓	✓
Copper	✗	░░░	✗	✗
Iron	✗	✓	░░░	✗
Zinc	✗	✓	✓	░░░

A tick (✓) indicates a reaction is occurring and a cross (✗) indicates no reaction.

- The parts of the table that are shaded show that the metal should not be placed in a solution of its own salt – for example, magnesium is not placed in magnesium sulfate solution.
- From the table it can seen that magnesium displaces the other three metals from their solutions, indicating that it is the most reactive of the four metals.
- Zinc displaces copper and iron from their solutions, but does not displace magnesium – showing that it is the next most reactive metal.
- Iron displaces only copper from its solution, so iron is the third most reactive metal.
- Copper does not displace any of the other metals from their solutions, indicating that it is the least reactive metal in this investigation.
- The reactivity in order from most reactive to least reactive is magnesium, zinc, iron, copper.

> **Exam tip**
> Questions often ask for reactivity in order from most reactive to least reactive, but be careful – some ask for the order from least reactive to most reactive.

> **Exam tip**
> Often an unfamiliar metal, such as chromium or cobalt, will be included and you may have to write a reactivity series based on the results from a table like the one above.
>
> Balanced symbol equations, ionic equations and observations for the reactions can also be asked for. Remember that 'heat released' is the most common observation for a displacement reaction.

Solids

Revised

When solid metal compounds (usually oxides) are heated with a solid metal, a displacement reaction can occur (and it is a redox reaction).

- The reactions are carried out with both the metal oxide and the metal in powder form to increase the contact between the solids.
- The reactions are carried out in a crucible with the same apparatus as shown for heating a metal in air shown on page 83.
- The reactions are exothermic.
- How exothermic a reaction is depends on how far apart the metals are in the reactivity series. The further apart the metals, the faster and more exothermic the reaction.
- If a mixture of magnesium powder and copper(II) oxide is heated strongly in a crucible, the crucible explodes. Powdered metals can be highly flammable.

Worked example 2

Zinc powder is mixed with black copper(II) oxide powder and heated in a crucible.

The reaction produces a blue-green glow and a yellow solid, which changes to white on cooling.

a) Write a balanced symbol equation for the reaction. [2]

b) Identify the ion that does not take part in the reaction (spectator ion). [1]

c) Write an ionic equation for the reaction. [2]

Answers

a) $Zn + CuO \rightarrow ZnO + Cu$ [2]

b) The oxide ion/O^{2-} [1]

c) $Zn + Cu^{2+} \rightarrow Zn^{2+} + Cu$ [2]

> **Exam tip**
>
> The observations for this reaction are important because the oxide formed is yellow when heated and changes to white on cooling – this is a pointer that the oxide formed is zinc oxide. The blue-green glow is caused by the presence of the copper(II) ions – this is similar to the flame test for copper(II) ions, see pages 70–71.

Reactivity series
Revised

From the reactions that we have seen, the reactivity series for the common metals can be written as:

K Na Ca Mg Al Zn Fe Cu

most reactive   least reactive

Precious metals like silver and gold are less reactive than copper.

> **Exam tip**
>
> You will need to learn this reactivity series and use it to predict whether or not a given reaction will occur.

Aluminium

The reactivity of aluminium is often 'hidden' because aluminium metal forms a **protective oxide layer** on its surface.

- A piece of aluminium foil added to an acid does not react – nor does it react with air or water or steam – because of the protective oxide layer.

- Powdered aluminium shows aluminium's true reactivity – alternatively the metal foil can have its oxide layer removed by washing with mercury(II) chloride solution (a very toxic compound).

- Aluminium is reasonably reactive but the protective aluminium oxide layer means it can be used for saucepans without reacting with food.

- Aluminium is a very low density metal and has many uses –the layer of aluminium oxide is often thickened in a process called anodising. This makes the aluminium even less likely to react.

> **Exam tip**
>
> When describing the reactivity of metals always state, for example, 'magnesium is more reactive than copper'. The most common mistake is to state simply 'magnesium is more reactive' but you must say more reactive than what.
>
> Under the same conditions, a more reactive metal will react faster than a less reactive metal.

1 Name the gas produced when calcium reacts with water. [1]

2 What is observed when potassium reacts with water? [4]

3 Write a balanced symbol equation for the reaction of potassium with water. [3]

4 What is observed when magnesium reacts with copper(II) sulfate solution? [3]

5 In the reaction of magnesium with steam, how is the steam generated in the apparatus? [2]

6 Copper metal reacts with silver(I) nitrate solution.

   a) Write a balanced symbol equation for the reaction. [3]

   b) Which ion does not take part in the reaction? [1]

   c) Write an ionic equation for the reaction. [3]

7 Explain why the reactivity of aluminium metal foil is lower than expected considering its position in the reactivity series. [3]

8 What is observed when magnesium metal is heated in air? [4]

9 State the colour of these substances:

   a) copper(II) oxide b) copper(II) sulfate solution c) magnesium. [3]

10 For the metals calcium, copper, zinc and aluminium:

   a) Which one burns with a red flame when heated in air? [1]

   b) Which one would displace magnesium from magnesium sulfate solution? [1]

   c) Place the metals in order of reactivity from most reactive to least reactive. [1]

11 Write a balanced symbol equation for the reaction of calcium with oxygen. [3]

The table below gives information on displacement reactions when solid metals are added to solutions of the metal nitrates. Use the information in the table to answer the questions that follow:

Metal \ Metal nitrate solution	Magnesium nitrate	Nickel(II) nitrate	Chromium(III) nitrate	Manganese(II) nitrate
Magnesium	/////	✓	✓	✓
Nickel	✗	/////	✗	✗
Chromium	✗	✓	/////	✗
Manganese	✗	✓	✓	/////

A tick (✓) indicates a reaction occuring and a cross (✗) indicates no reaction.

12 Write the metals in order of reactivity – from most reactive to least reactive. [1]

13 Write a balanced symbol equation for the reaction of chromium with nickel(II) nitrate solution forming chromium(III) nitrate as one of the products. [3]

14 Write an ionic equation for the reaction of magnesium with manganese(II) nitrate solution. [2]

15 Suggest why metal nitrates are often used in solution displacement reactions. [1]

10 Water

The physical properties of water

Revised

Note: The physical properties of water are required for Double Award Chemistry C1 (see page 75).

The main physical properties of water are:

- it is a colourless liquid at room temperature and pressure
- its melting point is 0 °C
- its boiling point is 100 °C.

Changes of state

The melting point of water is 0 °C. This means that water can be a liquid *and* a solid at 0 °C.

- Water changes from a liquid to a solid at 0 °C on heating – this is called melting.
- Water changes from a liquid to a solid at 0 °C on cooling – this is called freezing.
- Solid water is called ice.

The boiling point of water is 100 °C. This means that water can be a liquid *and* a gas at 100 °C.

- Water changes from a liquid to a gas at 100 °C on heating – this is called boiling.
- Water changes from a gas to a liquid at 100 °C on cooling – this is called condensing.
- Gaseous water is called water vapour.

Water undergoes evaporation at temperatures below its boiling point.

> **Exam tip**
> The physical properties of water are not enough to positively identify it. A chemical test must be used to do this.

> **Exam tip**
> Evaporation is the change of state from a liquid to a gas, below the boiling point.

Chemical tests for water

Revised

There are two main chemical tests for water:

- anhydrous copper(II) sulfate – white solid changes to blue
- **anhydrous cobalt(II) chloride** (or cobalt chloride paper) – pale blue changes to pink.

Hard water

Revised

Hard water is water that does not readily produce a lather with soap. Water that lathers easily with soap is called **soft water**. Hardness in water is caused by dissolved **Ca²⁺ ions** and/or **Mg²⁺ ions**.

Soap is sodium stearate – hard water reacts with soap to form a white **insoluble scum/solid**. Ca^{2+} (or Mg^{2+}) ions in the hard water react with the stearate ions from the soap, producing an insoluble scum called **calcium stearate** (or **magnesium stearate**).

● Hard water will eventually form a lather with soap but a lot more soap is required to produce a lather with hard water than with soft water.

● Hard water will form a lather with detergents.

There are two types of hardness in water – **temporary hardness and permanent hardness:**

● temporary hardness can be removed by boiling

● permanent hardness cannot be removed by boiling

● temporary hardness is caused by dissolved calcium hydrogen carbonate

● permanent hardness is caused by dissolved calcium sulfate or magnesium sulfate, or dissolved calcium chloride or magnesium chloride.

Testing for hardness

You should be able to describe a general test for hardness in water. You also need to be able to describe how to test a sample of water for permanent hardness and for temporary hardness. The general test for hardness is:

1 Add some soap solution to a sample of the water.

2 Shake the mixture well.

3 If scum forms, or there is no immediate lather, the water is hard.

The table shows the method of testing water to distinguish between the two types of hardness.

Testing hardness in water

Temporary hardness	Permanent hardness
1 Take a sample of the water and add soap solution	**1** Take a sample of the water and add soap solution
2 Shake the mixture – there should be no lather	**2** Shake the mixture – there should be no lather
3 Take another sample of the water and boil it	**3** Take another sample of the water and boil it
4 Add soap solution	**4** Add soap solution
5 Shake the mixture – there should be a lather	**5** Shake the mixture – there should be no lather

How temporary hardness arises in water

Limestone ($CaCO_3$) reacts with rainwater containing dissolved carbon dioxide to form calcium hydrogen carbonate solution. The equation for this reaction is:

$CaCO_3 + H_2O + CO_2 \rightarrow Ca(HCO_3)_2$

Many hard water regions have limestone features such as caves, stalagmites, stalactites and limestone pavements.

Removing hardness in water

Any method of removing hardness in water must remove the dissolved Ca^{2+} ions (or Mg^{2+} ions). This can be done by removing them from solution by precipitating them out as an insoluble solid (by adding washing soda or by boiling) or by exchanging them for Na^+ ions, which do not cause hardness.

Boiling

Boiling removes temporary hardness from water. Dissolved Ca^{2+} ions in the hard water are removed as insoluble $CaCO_3$. The equation for this reaction is:

$$Ca(HCO_3)_2(aq) \rightarrow CaCO_3(s) + CO_2(g) + H_2O(l)$$

Ion exchange

Ion exchange removes both permanent and temporary hardness in water. Dissolved Ca^{2+} ions (or Mg^{2+} ions) in the hard water are removed and replaced by Na^+ ions from the ion exchange resin – Na^+ ions do not cause hardness in water.

Washing soda (hydrated sodium carbonate)

Washing soda removes both permanent and temporary hardness in water. Dissolved Ca^{2+} ions (or Mg^{2+} ions) are removed from the hard water in a reaction with carbonate ions CO_3^{2-} from the washing soda to form insoluble $CaCO_3$ (or $MgCO_3$). The ionic equation for this reaction is:

$$Ca^{2+}(aq) + CO_3^{2-}(aq) \rightarrow CaCO_3(s)$$

> **Exam tip**
> This equation is the reverse of the formation of temporary hardness in water. This means you only have to learn one equation (for the formation of temporary hardness) – then reverse it for the removal of temporary hardness by boiling.

> **Exam tip**
> A precipitation reaction involves the ions in two solutions reacting to form an insoluble solid. The insoluble solid forms as a precipitate.

> **Exam tip**
> State symbols may be required for this equation. Remember that the ions on the left are in solution, so are '(aq)' and that the product is a solid '(s)'.

Advantages and disadvantages of hardness in water

Advantages

- Hard water tastes better.
- It is better for brewing beer.
- It is good for tanning leather.
- It provides calcium ions (Ca^{2+}) for healthy teeth and bones.

Disadvantages

- Hard water produces a scum with soap, which wastes soap.
- It produces fur (limescale, which is calcium carbonate), in kettles and hot-water pipes. This makes kettles less efficient and clogs up hot-water pipes.
- Dishwasher salt is needed to soften water in a dishwasher, which adds to the cost.

Interaction of substances with moist air

Note: *The terms 'desiccant' and 'deliquescent' are required only in Higher tier GCSE Chemistry).*

Many substances interact with moist air in a series of reactions with the oxygen and/or the water vapour in the air. These substances may be used as **desiccants** (drying agents).

Anhydrous calcium chloride

The white solid calcium chloride absorbs water from the air until, eventually, a colourless solution forms.

Silica gel

Self-indicating silica gel changes from blue to pink as it absorbs moisture from the air. (Normal silica gel is white and remains white when it absorbs moisture from the air.)

- A desiccant is a chemical that is **hygroscopic** (absorbs moisture from the air).
- Both calcium chloride and silica gel are desiccants.
- Desiccants are useful in the packaging of optical equipment and leather items where moisture would be a problem. Small packets containing silica gel are often found in the packaging of these items.
- Calcium chloride is also **deliquescent**.
- A deliquescent substance is one that absorbs moisture from the air – eventually absorbing enough to dissolve in it, forming a solution.

Fluoridation of drinking water

In some areas, fluoride ions are added to drinking water because they have been shown to help prevent tooth decay. This is also why 'fluoride' is added to toothpaste.

- Sodium fluoride is the main chemical used to provide fluoride ions.
- Some people object to fluoridation of drinking water because it is considered to be 'mass medication' with no choice for the consumer.
- Also, fluoridation has been linked to various diseases including stomach cancer.

Medical use of barium sulfate

- Barium compounds are very toxic.
- Barium sulfate does not allow X-rays to pass through it.
- Medical experts use barium sulfate on patients with stomach and intestinal problems to X-ray the stomach or bowel.
- Barium sulfate is chosen as a safe barium compound because it has a very low solubility in water so it cannot act as a poison in the human body.

1 What is meant by the term 'hard water'?   [2]

2 Name one chemical which causes temporary hardness in water.   [1]

3 What is the chemical name for washing soda?   [2]

4 State one advantage and one disadvantage of hardness in water.   [2]

5 What is observed when a sample of calcium chloride is left in the air for several days?   [2]

6 What is a 'desiccant'?   [1]

7 What colours are these hydrated salts:

    a) hydrated copper(II) sulfate; **b)** hydrated cobalt chloride?   [2]

8 Explain:

    a) how temporary hardness arises in water   [4]

    b) how washing soda removes hardness from water.   [4]

9 Explain why some people are opposed to fluoridation of drinking water supplies, and yet other people approve of it.   [2]

10 Four samples of water were tested for hardness by shaking with soap solution in a test tube. The height of the lather was measured. A fresh sample of each water was boiled and then re-tested with soap solution – the height of the lather was measured again. The results are recorded in the table.

Sample	Height of lather with initial sample	Height of lather with boiled sample
1	15	15
2	1	15
3	1	1
4	1	7

    a) Which of the samples is soft water?   [1]

    b) Which sample contained only permanent hardness?   [1]

    c) Which sample contained only temporary hardness?   [1]

    d) Explain your answer to part **c**.   [2]

Go online for the answers   Online

11 Different Types of Chemical Reactions

A chemical reaction can be recognised in one of the following ways:

● a colour change in the reaction

● the formation of a precipitate

● the formation of a gas

● a temperature change.

Exam tip

Not all chemical reactions show these changes but they are a good indicator that a chemical reaction has occurred. For example, when iron rusts there is a colour change from grey to brown. Rusting is a chemical reaction.

Types of chemical reactions

Revised ☐

There are three ways to classify a chemical reaction:

● energetics

● redox

● type of reaction.

Chemical reactions are either **exothermic** (give out heat to the surroundings) or endothermic (take in heat from the surroundings).

The table shows important exothermic and endothermic reactions that you need to be able to state as examples.

Exothermic	Endothermic
Neutralisation	Thermal decomposition
Displacement	Electrolysis
Combustion	Dehydration of hydrated salts
Hydration of anhydrous salts	
Rusting	

All chemicals possess **internal energy** in their bonds. Energy is required to break all types of bonds, and energy is released when all types of bonds are formed. This means that bond-breaking is endothermic and bond-making is exothermic.

Worked example 1

1   Methane burns in oxygen releasing energy to the surroundings:

$$CH_4 + 2O_2 \rightarrow CO_2 + 2H_2O$$

Explain why the combustion of methane is exothermic in terms of the energy of the bonds.   [5]

2   The reaction of hydrogen with iodine to form hydrogen iodide is endothermic:

$$H_2 + I_2 \rightarrow 2HI$$

Explain why this reaction is endothermic in terms of the energy of the bonds.   [5]

Answers

1   The energy required to break bonds [1] in the reactants, methane and oxygen, [1] is less [1] than the energy released when bonds are formed [1] in the products, carbon dioxide and water. [1]

2   The energy required to break bonds [1] in the reactants, hydrogen and iodine, [1] is more [1] than the energy released when bonds are formed [1] in the product, hydrogen iodide. [1]

Thermal decomposition   Revised ☐

Thermal decomposition is the process in which a substance breaks down when heated. All thermal decomposition reactions are endothermic.

Heating to constant mass ensures that *all* of the substance has been thermally decomposed. The most common thermal decomposition reactions are those of metal carbonates:

● some metal carbonates decompose on heating

● all Group 1 carbonates are stable to heat except lithium carbonate – for example, anhydrous sodium carbonate and potassium carbonate do not decompose when heated

● all Group 2 carbonates and transition metal carbonates decompose when heated.

The general equation for the thermal decomposition of a metal carbonate is:

metal carbonate → metal oxide + carbon dioxide

The two most common examples used are copper(II) carbonate and calcium carbonate.

Copper(II) carbonate ($CuCO_3$)

Copper(II) carbonate (often called 'copper carbonate') is a green solid.

● When copper(II) carbonate is heated it decomposes to the black solid copper(II) oxide and carbon dioxide gas is released.

● The solid loses mass due to the release of carbon dioxide gas:

$$CuCO_3 \rightarrow CuO + CO_2$$

Calcium carbonate (CaCO₃)

Calcium carbonate is a white solid with the formula $CaCO_3$.

● It is the main chemical in limestone and marble.

● It is insoluble in water.

● It is used to remove acidic impurities from the iron ore in the blast furnace.

● On heating, calcium carbonate decomposes to form calcium oxide and carbon dioxide:

$$CaCO_3 \rightarrow CaO + CO_2$$

● During heating the solid glows orange. There is a loss in mass due to the release of carbon dioxide gas.

Lime kiln   Revised ☐

Limestone (calcium carbonate) is decomposed into lime (calcium oxide) industrially in a **lime kiln**.

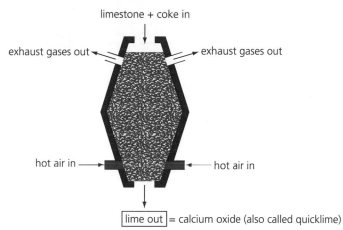

limestone + coke in

exhaust gases out ← → exhaust gases out

hot air in → ← hot air in

lime out = calcium oxide (also called quicklime)

↑ **A lime kiln**

● Hot air is blown into the lime kiln to burn the coke and heat the calcium carbonate until it decomposes.

● The exhaust gases mainly consist of carbon dioxide mixed with air.

Uses of calcium carbonate

Limestone is used in agriculture to neutralise acidity in soil water. Calcium carbonate reacts with acids reducing the acidity of the soil. It is also used as an antacid in the stomach to reduce excess stomach acidity.

Calcium carbonate is used in the extraction of iron. It decomposes to calcium oxide and this reacts with acidic impurities in the iron ore and removes them from the iron (page 155).

Mining limestone

Limestone is quarried and there are many positive and negative aspects to limestone quarrying.

Positive aspects of quarrying:

● provides employment

● provides better transport links

● provides landfill sites

● provides a local resource for construction and agriculture

● puts more money into the local economy.

Negative aspects of quarrying:

● destroys hedgerows, which are the habitat of many animals and birds

● creates an eyesore

● causes dust pollution

● causes noise pollution

● increases the traffic in the region.

> **Exam tip**
> Questions could be asked on all aspects of limestone – quarrying, lime kiln and reactions. It is a popular topic.

The atmosphere   Revised ☐

'Atmosphere' is the term used to describe the collection of gases that surrounds the Earth.

● The 'air' is the atmosphere near the surface.

● The composition of air has remained reasonably constant for about 200 million years with 79% nitrogen, 20% oxygen and a small percentage of other gases such as the noble gases (almost 1% argon), water vapour and carbon dioxide (usually quoted to be around 0.03%).

● The percentages vary from one place on Earth to another because the percentage of water vapour changes (greater in more humid climates) and the percentage of oxygen decreases with increasing altitude.

● Today's atmosphere is an oxidising one. Oxygen is the reactive part of the atmosphere and is used in biological and chemical processes such as respiration and combustion.

● The atmosphere on the Earth, further back than 200 million years ago, was a reducing one with large proportions of carbon dioxide, hydrogen sulfide, methane, ammonia and water vapour. This atmosphere was formed by intense volcanic activity.

● Changes in the atmosphere occurred slowly over millions of years due to several biological and chemical processes:

  ● photosynthesis (using up carbon dioxide and releasing oxygen)

  ● bacteria converting ammonia to nitrogen

  ● carbon dioxide dissolving in water and reacting to form carbonate rocks

  ● carbon, from carbon dioxide, being trapped in plants and animals forming fossil fuels over time.

- The composition of the atmosphere is still changing. Increased use of fossil fuels and deforestation are causing an increase in the percentage of carbon dioxide in the atmosphere.

- Carbon dioxide is a greenhouse gas and increased levels of the gas are thought to be causing an increase in the surface temperature of the Earth. This is thought to be causing an increase in sea levels, climate change, odd weather patterns and flooding of low level areas (see page 134).

- There is continued debate over the causes of climate change/global warming between environmental scientists, governments and the major users and suppliers of fossil fuels.

The Earth's surface

Revised

The German scientist Alfred Wegener proposed a theory of continental drift in 1912. This suggested that the continents on the surface of the Earth are moving and that they were one single large land mass millions of years ago – since then they have drifted away from each other.

Wegener used the following evidence to help explain his theory:

- The shape of continents – e.g. South America would fit almost exactly into Africa.

- The fossils found in continents that he proposed had once been joined were very similar.

- There were similar species of animals found in continents that he proposed had once been joined, and none of these animals had ever been able to survive in water.

Wegener's theory was not readily accepted by other scientists because he could not provide a mechanism to explain how the continents moved.

- In the 1950s, advances in science helped the discovery that the Earth's crust is made up of large plates (called tectonic plates) that float on the mantle. The plates are less dense than the mantle, so they float. The plates move about because of convection currents in the liquid mantle.

- Changes in the surface of the Earth occur with dramatic and devastating effect at the boundaries between tectonic plates.

- Plates may collide directly with each other and mountain ranges can be formed at these boundaries.

- Plates are pulled apart from each other and this can cause the formation of volcanoes, where the liquid part of the mantle, called magma, reaches the surface. At the Earth's surface magma is called 'lava'.

- Plates that are trying to move past each other may remain in one position for years but when they do eventually move they cause earthquakes.

- The Earth's surface is still changing today due to the movement of the tectonic plates.

Redox

A **redox reaction** is one in which **oxidation** and **reduction** occur at the same time. Oxidation and reduction can be defined in one of three ways as shown in the in table.

Note: *Redox in terms of electrons is Higher tier.*

Oxidation	Reduction
Gain of oxygen	Loss of oxygen
Loss of hydrogen	Gain of hydrogen
Loss of electrons	Gain of electrons

- Many reactions can be simply described as oxidation or reduction in terms of the change in the oxygen or hydrogen content.
- Other reactions can only be described in terms of electrons lost or gained.
- Reduction is the reverse of oxidation.

> **Exam tip**
>
> The answer to a simple 'change in oxygen or hydrogen content' question is worth 2 or 3 marks. You should always give the following 3-mark answer:
> - species (name) undergoes gain/loss in oxygen/hydrogen
> - gain/loss of oxygen/hydrogen is oxidation/reduction
> - species (name) has been oxidised/reduced.

Worked example 2

1   Explain why this reaction is described as reduction:

$H_2 + Cl_2 \rightarrow 2HCl$ [3]

2   Magnesium burns in air according to the equation:

$2Mg + O_2 \rightarrow 2MgO$

Explain why this reaction is described as oxidation. [3]

Answers

1   Chlorine gains hydrogen [1]; gain of hydrogen is reduction [1]; chlorine has been reduced. [1]

2   Magnesium gains oxygen [1]; gain of oxygen is oxidation [1]; magnesium is oxidised [1]

   or magnesium loses electrons [1]; loss of electrons is oxidation [1]; magnesium is oxidised. [1]

> **Exam tip**
>
> The first question is worth 3 marks because you need to identify which species is being reduced, as well as describing the reduction. The second question can be answered in two ways – either in terms of oxygen or in terms of electrons.

Redox and displacement reactions

A displacement reaction (see page 86) is one in which a **more reactive element** will form ions and cause **ions of a less reactive element** to change to atoms. This process involves the transfer of electrons. The more reactive element displaces the less reactive element from a compound.

- There are two main types of displacement reaction:
  - a solid metal reacting with a solution containing metal ions
  - a solid metal reacting with a solid metal oxide.
- One species will lose electrons and one will gain electrons:
  - the loss of electrons is called **oxidation**
  - the gain of electrons is called **reduction**.
- When both oxidation and reduction reactions occur in the same reaction, the overall reaction is described as a **redox reaction**.

Displacement reactions involving solutions

Example 1

Magnesium metal reacts when placed in a solution of copper(II) sulfate. Explain, in terms of electrons, why this reaction is described as a redox reaction.

To answer this question, use the following process:

Balanced symbol equation: $Mg + CuSO_4 \rightarrow MgSO_4 + Cu$

Ionic equation: $Mg + Cu^{2+} \rightarrow Mg^{2+} + Cu$

Spectator ion: SO_4^{2-} (does not take part in the reaction and is the same in reactants and products)

Half-equations: $Mg \rightarrow Mg^{2+} + 2e^-$ oxidation

Magnesium atoms lose electrons, and loss of electrons is oxidation.

$Cu^{2+} + 2e^- \rightarrow Cu$ reduction

Copper(II) ions gain electrons, and gain of electrons is reduction.

The reaction is a **redox reaction** because both oxidation and reduction are occurring simultaneously.

> **Exam tip**
>
> Most questions are of the type in Example 1. Observations are usually only asked for when it is a question involving copper(II) ions in solution, because this involves a colour change. There can be up to 7 marks for a question in which you are asked to explain why a reaction is described as a redox reaction in terms of electrons.
>
> - metal loses electrons or $M \rightarrow M^{2+} + 2e^-$ [2] and the loss of electrons is oxidation [1]
> - metal ion gains electrons or $X^{2+} + 2e^- \rightarrow X$ [2] and the gain of electrons is reduction [1]
> - oxidation and reduction occurring simultaneously in the same reaction is redox. [1]
>
> A common error is failing to make your answer specific to the reaction in the question. You must state what gains oxygen/loses electrons for oxidation, and then state that oxidation is the gain of oxygen or the loss of electrons.

Displacement reactions between solids

When solids metal compounds (often oxides) are heated with a solid metal, a displacement reaction can occur – it is a redox reaction (see page 87).

Example 2

Zinc powder is mixed with black copper(II) oxide powder and heated in a crucible.

The reaction produces a blue-green glow and a yellow solid, which changes to white on cooling.

Balanced symbol equation: $Zn + CuO \rightarrow ZnO + Cu$

Ionic equation: $Zn + Cu^{2+} \rightarrow Zn^{2+} + Cu$

Spectator ion: O^{2-} (does not take part in the reaction and is the same in reactants and products.)

Half-equations: $Zn \rightarrow Zn^{2+} + 2e^-$ oxidation.

Zinc atoms lose electrons, and loss of electrons is oxidation.

$Cu^{2+} + 2e^- \rightarrow Cu$ reduction.

Copper(II) ions gain electrons, and gain of electrons is reduction

This reaction is a **redox reaction** because both oxidation and reduction are occurring simultaneously.

Rusting

Revised

Rust is hydrated iron(III) oxide, sometimes written $Fe_2O_3.xH_2O$. When iron is exposed to air (oxygen) and moisture (water in the air), the iron rusts.

Note: *Steel is an alloy of iron containing between 0.2 and 2% carbon. Steel is stronger than iron. The iron in steel also rusts.*

An investigation to determine the factors that cause rusting is shown below:

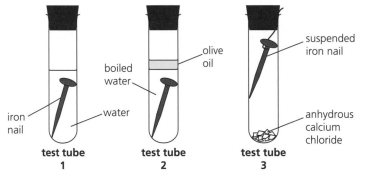

⬆ **Investigating the factors that cause rusting**

- Test tube 1 has air and water present.
- Test tube 2 has had the air removed from the water (by boiling), so only water is present. The olive oil prevents gases from the air dissolving in the water.
- Test tube 3 contains anhydrous calcium chloride, which removes the water vapour from the air, so only air is present. The nail is suspended to prevent contact between it and the calcium chloride.

The test tubes are left for several days and the iron nail rusts in only test tube 1. This indicates that both air and water are required for rusting.

Prevention of rusting

Iron and steel are used extensively in construction and rusting is a major problem due to the cost of replacing them. Rust is unsightly and also dangerous because it weakens the metal. Rusting can be prevented in a variety of ways. Methods fall into three groups.

1 Preventing the surface of the iron coming into contact with water and air by using a barrier or protective layer:

- paint is used to protect cars, bridges and railings
- oil or grease is used to protect tools and machinery
- plastic coating – such as that used to cover bicycle handlebars, garden chairs and dish racks. Car manufacturers are increasingly using plastic in cars to reduce the problem of rust.
- plating with another metal
  - tin is used in making cans for food – these are made from steel and are coated on both sides with a thin layer of tin. Tin is unreactive and non-toxic. It is deposited on the steel by electrolysis.
  - chromium is used to coat steel giving it a shiny, attractive appearance. This is used for some vehicle bumpers and bicycle handlebars. Chromium can be applied by electrolysis.

2 Putting a more reactive metal in contact with the iron or steel. The more reactive metal reacts first, leaving the iron intact.

- Bars of magnesium are attached to the sides of ships, oil rigs and underwater pipes to prevent rusting. The magnesium **corrodes** instead of the iron or steel and must be replaced with fresh magnesium periodically. This method of rust prevention is called **sacrificial protection**.
- Iron can be coated in zinc – this is called **galvanising**. Zinc is more reactive than iron and oxidises to form a layer of zinc oxide readily. Galvanising protects by sacrificial protection if the surface is scratched, and also the zinc oxide provides a barrier to air and water.

Exam tip

Only iron and steel rust, other metals corrode.

3 Alloying – an alloy is a mixture of two or more elements, at least one of which is a metal. Alloys have metallic properties. Alloys are often stronger and more resistant to corrosion than the pure metals they are made from. Stainless steel is an alloy that is resistant to corrosion.

Common oxidation and reduction reactions

Revised

Combustion

Combustion happens when a substance burns in air, producing oxides and releasing heat. The elements in the fuel (usually hydrogen and carbon) are oxidised to water and carbon dioxide (if the combustion is complete). For example, the complete combustion of carbon is represented by:

$$C + O_2 \rightarrow CO_2$$

Carbon gains oxygen; gain of oxygen is oxidation; carbon is oxidised.

If the supply of oxygen is limited, the carbon is only oxidised to carbon monoxide – this is called incomplete combustion. For example, the incomplete combustion of carbon is represented by:

$$2C + O_2 \rightarrow 2CO$$

Carbon still gains oxygen; gain of oxygen is oxidation; carbon is oxidised.

Elements reacting directly with oxygen

Magnesium

Observations: Magnesium is a grey metal that burns with a bright white light, releasing heat and forming a white powder.

$2Mg + O_2 \rightarrow 2MgO$

Sulfur

Observations: Sulfur is a yellow powder which melts to a red liquid and burns with a blue flame releasing heat and forming a colourless, pungent and choking gas called sulfur dioxide:

$S + O_2 \rightarrow SO_2$

Exam tip

Remember that magnesium burns with a bright **white** light and sulfur burns with a **blue** flame. The colour of the flame for magnesium is often left out and the colour of the flame for sulfur is often incorrect.

Reducing copper(II) oxide

Metal oxides such as copper(II) oxide (often called 'copper oxide') can be reduced using hydrogen gas. The hydrogen is passed over the heated metal oxide.

Observations: Black copper oxide changes to a pink colour; condensation collects inside the tube.

$CuO + H_2 \rightarrow Cu + H_2O$

- The copper(II) oxide is reduced to copper because the copper(II) oxide loses oxygen; loss of oxygen is reduction.

- The hydrogen is oxidised to water because hydrogen gains oxygen; gain of oxygen is oxidation.

- This reaction is a **redox reaction** because both oxidation and reduction are occurring simultaneously.

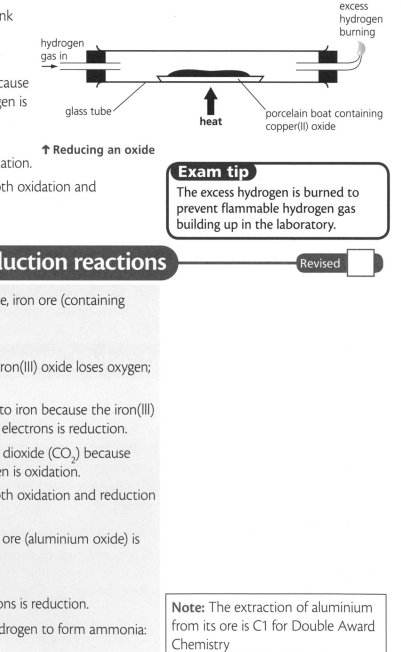

↑ **Reducing an oxide**

Exam tip

The excess hydrogen is burned to prevent flammable hydrogen gas building up in the laboratory.

Industrial oxidation and reduction reactions

Revised

1 In the manufacture of iron in the blast furnace, iron ore (containing iron(III) oxide) is reduced to iron:

$Fe_2O_3 + 3CO \rightarrow 2Fe + 3CO_2$ (see page 155)

- Iron(III) oxide is reduced to iron because the iron(III) oxide loses oxygen; loss of oxygen is reduction.

  OR iron(III) ions in iron(III) oxide are reduced to iron because the iron(III) ions gain electrons ($Fe^{3+} + 3e^- \rightarrow Fe$); gain of electrons is reduction.

- Carbon monoxide (CO) is oxidised to carbon dioxide (CO_2) because carbon monoxide gains oxygen; gain of oxygen is oxidation.

- This reaction is a **redox reaction** because both oxidation and reduction are occurring simultaneously.

2 In the manufacture of aluminium, aluminium ore (aluminium oxide) is reduced to aluminium by electrolysis:

$Al^{3+} + 3e^- \rightarrow Al$ (see page 154)

Aluminium ions gain electrons; gain of electrons is reduction.

3 In the Haber process, nitrogen reacts with hydrogen to form ammonia:

$N_2 + 3H_2 \rightleftharpoons 2NH_3$ (see page 119)

Nitrogen gains hydrogen; gain of hydrogen is reduction.

Note: The extraction of aluminium from its ore is C1 for Double Award Chemistry

1 What do these terms mean:

   a) exothermic; **b)** endothermic? [2]

2 Indicate which of the following reactions are exothermic and which are endothermic:

   a) thermal decomposition of $CaCO_3$

   b) complete combustion of methane

   c) dehydration of hydrated copper(II) sulfate. [3]

3 Who proposed the theory of continental drift? [1]

4 Name **one** metal that can be used to prevent rusting by sacrificial protection. [1]

5 What is meant by these following terms:

   a) combustion **[3]**; **b)** rust **[2]**; **c)** redox? **[1]**

6 Copper(II) carbonate breaks down on heating.

   a) Write a balanced symbol equation for the reaction. [2]

   b) What colour change would you observe when copper(II) carbonate is heated? [2]

7 When zinc reacts with copper(II) sulfate solution, a displacement reaction occurs. The zinc is converted to zinc ions and the copper ions are converted to copper atoms.

   a) Write a half equation for the conversion of zinc atoms to zinc ions. [2]

   b) Write a half equation for the conversion of copper ions to copper atoms. [2]

   c) State which of the above half equations you have written is oxidation. [1]

8 Name one metal carbonate that cannot be decomposed by heating. [1]

9 In the Haber process, ammonia is formed from nitrogen and hydrogen:

$N_2 + 3H_2 \rightleftharpoons 2NH_3$

Explain why the nitrogen is described as being reduced in this reaction. [2]

10 What would you observe when sulfur burns in air? [3]

11 What **two** conditions are necessary for rusting to occur? [2]

12 Lead(II) nitrate decomposes to form lead(II) oxide, nitrogen dioxide and oxygen. Write a balanced symbol equation for the reaction. [3]

13 State three pieces of evidence that support the theory of continental drift. [3]

14 From the following gases:

   hydrogen   oxygen   nitrogen   carbon dioxide   argon

   a) which is gained in a reduction reaction [1]

   b) which is gained in an oxidation reaction [1]

   c) which makes up the largest proportion of the atmosphere on the Earth in the present day? [1]

15 A piece of magnesium ribbon was wrapped around an iron nail to prevent it from rusting. Explain how the magnesium protects the iron from rusting. [2]

Go online for the answers

Online

12 Rates of Reactions

The **rate** (speed at which reactants change into products) of a chemical reaction depends on:

- the surface area or size of solid particles
- the concentration of solutions
- the temperature
- the presence of a catalyst.

Each of these factors can be studied experimentally. There are different methods of measuring rate – all of them measure a quantity against time; for example, a change in mass or a change in gas volume. Other factors, such as light and pressure, may affect the rate of some chemical reactions but these are not studied practically at GCSE.

Reactions used in rate of reaction experiments   Revised

The following reactions are the most often used:

1 A metal reacting with a dilute acid – for example, zinc or magnesium with dilute hydrochloric acid or dilute sulfuric acid. All these reactions produce hydrogen gas:

$$Mg + 2HCl \rightarrow MgCl_2 + H_2 \quad \text{or} \quad Mg + H_2SO_4 \rightarrow MgSO_4 + H_2$$
$$Zn + 2HCl \rightarrow ZnCl_2 + H_2 \quad \text{or} \quad Zn + H_2SO_4 \rightarrow ZnSO_4 + H_2$$

2 Marble chips (calcium carbonate) reacting with dilute hydrochloric acid. This reaction produces carbon dioxide gas:

$$CaCO_3 + 2HCl \rightarrow CaCl_2 + H_2O + CO_2$$

3 The catalytic decomposition of hydrogen peroxide (H_2O_2). This reaction produces oxygen gas:

$$2H_2O_2 \rightarrow 2H_2O + O_2$$

The catalyst is manganese dioxide, MnO_2 (also called manganese(IV) oxide).

> ### Exam tip
> The production of gases in these reactions allows the rate to be monitored in several ways. The mass of the reaction will decrease as the gas is released. The volume of gas produced could be measured. The time for the reaction to stop (fizzing) could also be measured.

Measuring a change in mass   Revised

The reaction between marble chips (calcium carbonate, $CaCO_3$) and hydrochloric acid can be used to investigate how the size of solid particles affects the rate of the reaction.

Mass is 'lost' during this reaction because carbon dioxide escapes from the reaction vessel. Recording the loss in mass over a certain period of time at regular intervals using the apparatus shown gives an indication of the rate of the reaction. The cotton wool stops any liquid loss from the flask – there is **effervescence** (bubbling), which can cause the solution to splash out.

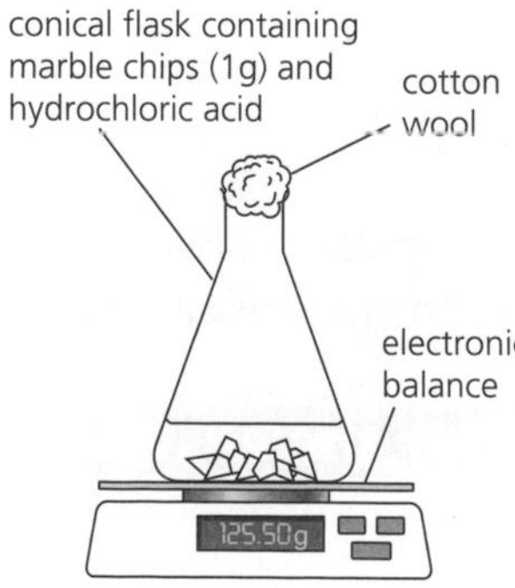

conical flask containing marble chips (1g) and hydrochloric acid

cotton wool

electronic balance

125.50g

↑ **Investigating the effect of particle size on reaction rate**

1g of large marble chips was used first; and then the experiment was repeated using 1g of smaller chips. The results are shown in the graph of mass plotted against time.

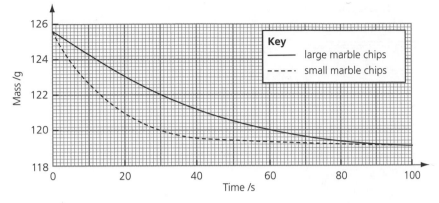

↑ **The effect of particle size on reaction rate**

● From the graph you can see that the reaction occurred more rapidly with smaller marble chips. The smaller marble chips have a much larger surface area to make contact with the acid. This causes an increased rate of reaction.

● As the same mass of marble chips and the same volume and concentration of acid were used, the graphs for both reactions start and level off at the same masses.

● The steeper initial slope of the curve for small marble chips indicates that the mass is decreasing more quickly. So the **rate of reaction** is higher with smaller solid particles.

Measuring gas volume

Revised ▢

If a reaction produces a gas, a good method of measuring a reaction rate is by collecting the gas in a gas syringe over a period of time. The diagram shows the apparatus used to produce and collect carbon dioxide in the reaction between marble chips and hydrochloric acid. The volume of carbon dioxide is measured by taking readings from the gas syringe at various time intervals.

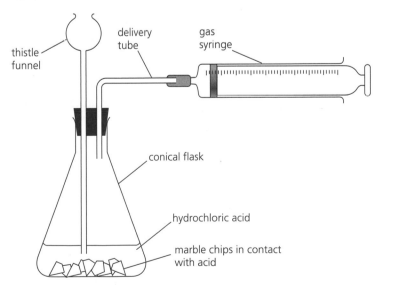

↑ **Investigating rate of reaction by measuring the volume of a gas produced**

Note: *An inverted measuring cylinder filled with water over a beehive shelf in a trough of water could also be used to measure the volume of gas produced.*

A typical graph obtained in experiments such as this is shown here.

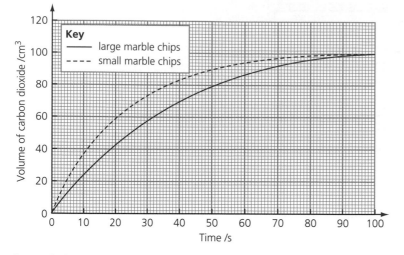

↑ Graph showing how particle size affects the volume of gas produced

● The volume of gas produced increases more rapidly initially when small marble chips are used.

● The curves on the graph start and end at the same gas volume because the same mass of marble chips and the same volume and concentration of hydrochloric acid are used.

Measuring the time for a reaction to be completed
Revised

In reactions that produce a gas or in which a solid disappears, the time until the reaction stops can be measured. For a reaction that produces a gas, the time for the reaction to finish can be determined by:

● reading the time when the mass first reaches its minimum on a graph of mass against time.

● reading the time when the gas volume first reaches its maximum on a graph of gas volume against time.

● timing the reaction until you see that the production of gas has stopped.

For a reaction in which a solid disappears, the reaction can be timed until no more solid can be seen in the reaction vessel.

Calculating rate from time
Revised

A value for rate can be calculated from the time for the reaction to be completed:

$$\text{rate} = \frac{1}{\text{time}}.$$ The units of rate are s^{-1}.

Planning an investigation

Planning an investigation involves several steps but making an initial prediction and ensuring that the investigation is a fair test are both important.

Predictions about the outcome of an investigation are often written in the form:

- as **quantity one** increases, **quantity two** increases/decreases. Quantity two will either increase or decrease as quantity one increases.

For an investigation into the effects of changing the concentration of hydrochloric acid on the rate of reaction with magnesium ribbon, the prediction could read: as **the concentration of the acid** increases, the **rate of the reaction** increases.

A 'fair test' is the phrase used for an investigation in which one variable is changed (the independent variable), one variable is measured (the dependent variable) and all other variables are kept the same (controlled variables).

> **Exam tip**
>
> This section is most often examined in controlled assessment tasks.

Validity and reliability of data collection

- *Validity* is part of the overall design of the experiment. Suppose an experiment uses two concentrations of acid ($0.2\,mol/dm^3$ and $0.25\,mol/dm^3$) to determine the link between concentration and rate of reaction. The results obtained from this may not be valid because of the limited range of the concentrations. The validity could be improved by using a greater number and range of concentrations of acid.

- *Reliability* depends on whether or not the same result could be obtained again if the experiment were to be repeated. Measuring the time for a reaction to reach completion by simply observing the reaction may not be reliable because the results are judged by the observer. Measuring the gas volume or the change in mass can produce more reliable results because the time when the reaction finishes is determined by the apparatus used in the experiment – i.e. a gas syringe or an electronic balance.

- An *anomaly* is a piece of data that does not match the pattern shown in the rest of the investigation. Many anomalies are easily spotted from a graph – they are indicated by points which do not fall on or close to the line of best fit.

Explaining the effects of temperature and concentration on reaction rate

Reactions happen when reacting atoms, molecules or ions collide with each other. Only *some* of the collisions result in a reaction and these are called successful collisions. The minimum energy that the colliding particles need to react is called the **activation energy**. An increase in temperature increases the rate of most reactions.

> **Exam tip**
>
> The term 'activation energy' is not required for Double Award Chemistry but may be useful in explaining a prediction in controlled assessment.

At a *higher temperature*:

● the particles have more energy and move faster

● this leads to more collisions between particles

● and so more successful collisions in a given period of time – more particles have more energy than the activation energy

● this increases the rate of the reaction.

At a *higher concentration* of solution:

● there are more particles present in the same volume

● this leads to more collisions between particles

● and so more successful collisions in a given period of time

● this increases the rate of the reaction

Worked example 1

An increase in the concentration of hydrochloric acid increases the rate of reaction of the acid with magnesium ribbon. Explain, in terms of particles, how this occurs. [4]

Answer

As the concentration of hydrochloric acid increases, the number of hydrogen ions increases. [1] This increases the number of collisions, [1] which increases the number of successful collisions [1] in a given period of time [1].

Investigating the effect of the presence of a catalyst

Revised

A reaction commonly used for the study of the effect of a catalyst is the decomposition of hydrogen peroxide using manganese(IV) oxide, MnO_2, as a catalyst. The reaction can be monitored using a gas syringe to collect and measure the volume of oxygen gas produced. Graphs of gas volume against time are then drawn.

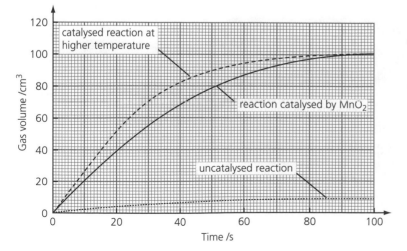

↑ **The volume of oxygen collected for the decomposition of hydrogen peroxide**

From the graph, the catalysed reaction happens at a faster rate than the uncatalysed reaction, and the catalysed reaction at a higher temperature occurs at the highest rate of the reactions studied.

Points to note for the graph at higher temperature when all other factors are kept the same (i.e. concentration, volume, etc.) are:

- the gas volume starts at zero
- the gas volume is higher at every time
- the line on the graph levels off earlier
- but ends at same final gas volume

Metal + acid reactions   Revised

The effects of changes in both temperature and concentration can be studied using two other reactions:

- zinc with dilute acid
- magnesium with dilute acid.

Both reactions produce hydrogen gas so gas volume can be used as a measure of the rate of the reaction.

- A change of temperature will alter the shape of the gas volume against time graph – it doesn't make any difference whether the acid or the metal is in excess.

- A change of concentration of the acid will alter the shape of the gas volume graph, but the final gas volume will be the same because the acid will be in excess.

The graphs for the reaction with magnesium are shown for three different temperatures of the acid.

Note: *The same four points are true for the higher temperature as explained above and the opposite is true of lower temperatures.*

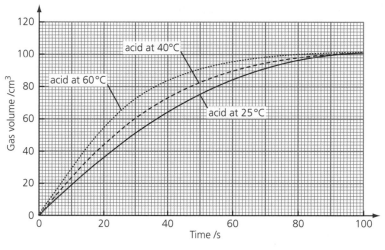

↑ **Gas volume against time graphs at different temperatures**

Catalysts   Revised

A **catalyst** is a substance that increases the rate of a chemical reaction without being used up.

- Remember that activation energy is the energy that the colliding particles must have in order to react – i.e. to achieve a successful collision.

- Catalysts work by lowering the activation energy, which increases the number of successful collisions in a given period of time – this increases the rate of a reaction.

- The mass of catalyst will be the same at the end of the reaction as at the start because a catalyst is not used up.

Some catalysts

Reaction/ industrial process	Catalyst
Decomposition of hydrogen peroxide	Manganese(IV) oxide, MnO_2
Contact process (sulfuric acid manufacture)	Vanadium(V) oxide, V_2O_5
Haber process (ammonia manufacture)	Iron

In any industrial process, the manufacturers want to achieve the maximum **yield** of product in the shortest time possible, with the minimum of expense.

● Changes in temperature and pressure and the presence of a catalyst can increase the yield of a product and the rate at which it is formed.

● However, these factors can be expensive and a **cost analysis** must be carried out to make sure there are significant benefits, in terms of profit, to justify the expense.

● High pressure for gases is expensive to apply and expensive in terms of the containers needed – it is also dangerous for staff working on the site.

● The rate of a chemical reaction increases with increasing temperature but for some reactions, a lower temperature gives a greater yield. So if a manufacturer uses a lower temperature then the rate is lowered even if more of the product is obtained (but in a much longer time period). A **compromise temperature** is used that allows enough of the product to be made in as short a time period as possible.

● Development of more effective catalysts can increase the profit of an industrial process.

A more effective catalyst can help make an industrial process more cost effective and environmentally sustainable in three ways:

1 *Using less energy* – the energy needed in an industrial process increases the cost of production, and also the environmental impact, because the energy may be obtained from combustion of fossil fuels. A better catalyst may reduce the temperature and pressure required.

Also the following should be considered in terms of reducing energy consumption in industrial processes:

● The use of renewable sources of energy would improve the environmental impact of these processes.

● Sometimes energy is produced in one step of an industrial process and this energy can be used in another step in the process – for example, some of the heat released by burning sulfur in the first step of the Contact process for the production of sulfuric acid (see page 125) can be used to generate the elevated temperature needed in the second step.

2 *Using renewable raw materials* – these are more environmentally sustainable because the human race continues to use up many non-renewable raw materials such as crude oil (see pages 129–130).

3 *Being carried out in fewer steps* – many steps in an industrial process generate waste. Keeping the number of steps to a minimum saves resources.

Revision Questions

Tested

1 Name the catalyst used in the decomposition of hydrogen peroxide. [1]

2 State two ways in which a more effective catalyst can make an industrial process more cost effective. [2]

3 What piece of apparatus is used to measure gas volume? [1]

4 What catalyst is used for the industrial production of ammonia in the Haber process? [1]

5 State the effect of an increase in temperature on the rate of a chemical reaction. [1]

6 What is meant by the term 'catalyst'? [3]

7 What gas is produced when magnesium reacts with dilute hydrochloric acid? [1]

8 Apart from temperature and concentration, name one factor that will affect the rate of a chemical reaction. [1]

9 Briefly describe a method you could use to determine the rate of reaction between marble chips and dilute hydrochloric acid. [2]

10 Explain, in terms of particles, how increasing the temperature of dilute hydrochloric acid would affect the rate of reaction with zinc metal. [4]

11 The graph shows the volume of hydrogen gas produced against time for the reaction of zinc with 25.0 cm^3 of 0.5 mol/dm^3 hydrochloric acid at 25 °C. All the zinc was used up in the reaction.

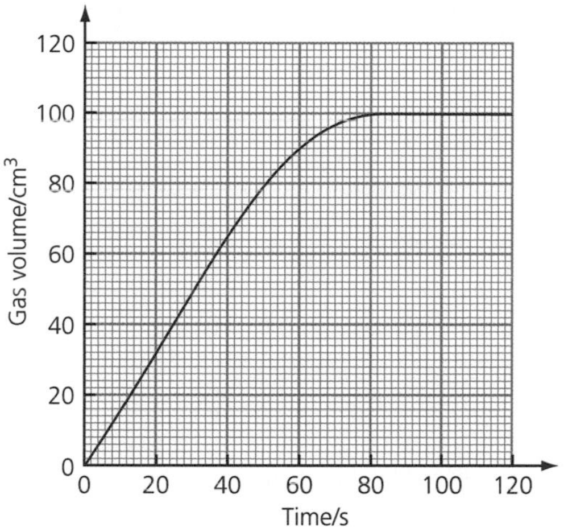

a) At what time did the reaction end? [1]

b) What volume of gas had been produced at 50 seconds? [1]

c) At what time was the gas volume 40 cm^3? [1]

d) Copy the graph and then sketch on it the line you would expect to obtain if the temperature was increased to 40 °C and all other factors were kept the same. Label your line 'A'. [3]

e) If the concentration of the acid was reduced to 0.4 mol/dm^3 and the same mass of zinc was added at 25 °C, sketch a second line on your graph that you would expect to obtain if all the zinc is again used up. Label this one 'B'. [3]

Go online for the answers

Online

13 Non-metals

Note: *For Double Award Chemistry the test for water using anhydrous copper(II) sulfate is required in this section.*

Much of the non-metal chemistry section in the specification involves gases and for each gas it is important to know the following:

● the methods of preparation
● the physical properties
● the chemical properties
● the chemical tests.

Preparation of the gases
Revised ▢

You need to know:

● the reagents
● the apparatus used to prepare these gases:
  ● hydrogen
  ● carbon dioxide
  ● oxygen
  ● nitrogen by removing other gases from air
● the way in which a gas is collected.

Collecting insoluble gases
Revised ▢

The diagram shows how gases that are **insoluble** in water, or have a low solubility in water, can be collected. This is called **collection over water**.

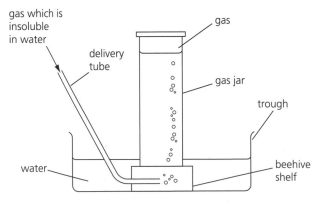

gas which is insoluble in water

delivery tube

gas

gas jar

trough

water

beehive shelf

↑ **Collecting a gas over water**

Collecting soluble gases
Revised ▢

Gases that are soluble in water are collected by **displacement** of air and the **density** of the gas compared to air must be considered:

● soluble gases that are denser than air are collected by **downward delivery**

- soluble gases that are less dense than air must be collected by **upward delivery**.

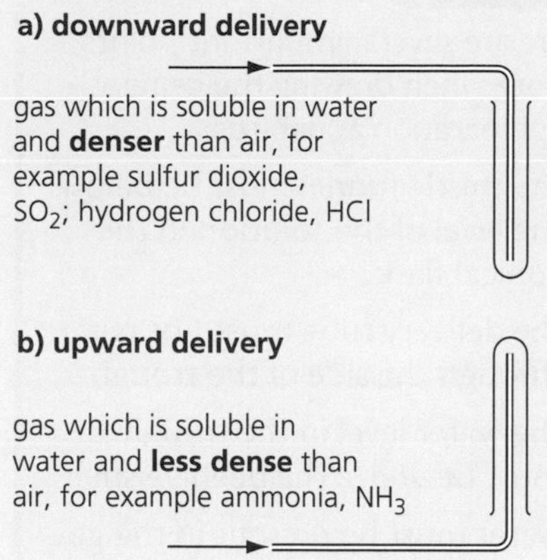

a) downward delivery

gas which is soluble in water and **denser** than air, for example sulfur dioxide, SO_2; hydrogen chloride, HCl

b) upward delivery

gas which is soluble in water and **less dense** than air, for example ammonia, NH_3

↑ **Collecting a gas: a) by downward delivery, b) by upward delivery**

Hydrogen
Revised

Physical properties of hydrogen

Hydrogen is a colourless, odourless gas that is insoluble in water and less dense than air. Hydrogen is diatomic, H_2.

Chemical properties of hydrogen

1 Hydrogen gas burns explosively.

   Observations: Burns with a clean, blue flame producing water vapour, which may condense to form a colourless liquid on glass.

   $2H_2 + O_2 \rightarrow 2H_2O$

2 Hydrogen reduces heated copper(II) oxide (see page 104).

   Observations: Black copper oxide changes to pink; condensation appears.

   $CuO + H_2 \rightarrow Cu + H_2O$

   Apparatus: See page 104

3 Hydrogen reacts with nitrogen forming ammonia in the Haber process – see pages 119–120.

   $N_2 + 3H_2 \rightleftharpoons 2NH_3$

Preparation of hydrogen

Hydrogen is prepared using zinc (or magnesium) and dilute hydrochloric acid:

$Zn + 2HCl \rightarrow ZnCl_2 + H_2$
$Mg + 2HCl \rightarrow MgCl_2 + H_2$

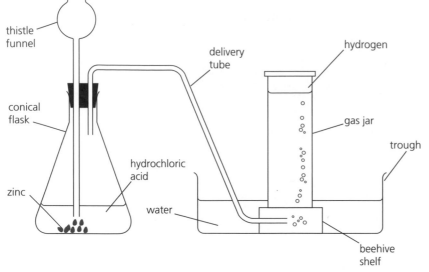

thistle funnel
delivery tube
hydrogen
conical flask
gas jar
trough
hydrochloric acid
zinc
water
beehive shelf

↑ **Preparing and collecting hydrogen gas**

Exam tip

There are several important points to note when drawing the general gas preparation apparatus:

- the thistle funnel must be below the level of the solution in the conical flask
- the delivery tube must not cut through the side of the trough
- the water level in the trough must be *above* the beehive shelf
- water must be present in the gas jar.

● Hydrogen is collected over water because it is **insoluble** in water.

● The reaction of dilute hydrochloric acid with magnesium is more vigorous and is not recommended for controlled preparation of hydrogen.

Test for hydrogen

Method: Apply a lighted splint.

Test result: It burns with a squeaky pop.

$$2H_2 + O_2 \rightarrow 2H_2O$$

Uses of hydrogen

● Meteorological (weather) balloons

● Rocket engines

● As a clean fuel.

Hydrogen as a clean fuel

Hydrogen is described as a 'clean' fuel because the only product of combustion (water) is non-polluting.

● Hydrogen can be produced from the electrolysis of water – but this requires electricity. The electricity can be generated from combustion of fossil fuels or renewable sources of energy such as tidal, solar, wave or hydroelectric. The use of renewable sources of energy increases the potential of hydrogen as a clean fuel.

● Hydrogen can be used to power vehicles and would be supplied to consumers in liquid form. Keeping hydrogen as a liquid requires energy and specialised storage.

● Hydrogen is very flammable and so high-level safety controls would have to be in place to protect users from the risk of explosion.

Technology is advancing to improve the supply, storage and use of hydrogen.

Carbon is often used in school laboratories as powdered charcoal – this is a black solid. Charcoal is an impure form of carbon.

Carbon exists as two distinct forms called diamond and graphite. These have identical atoms but it is the way in which the atoms are bonded together that makes the forms different. Different forms/structures of the same element in the same physical state are called **allotropes**.

Chemical properties of carbon

Combustion – carbon burns in an excess of oxygen

Observations: Carbon burns in a plentiful supply of oxygen with an orange flame forming a colourless, odourless gas called carbon dioxide.

$C + O_2 \rightarrow CO_2$

In a limited supply of oxygen, colourless carbon monoxide is formed.

$2C + O_2 \rightarrow 2CO$

In a limited supply of oxygen, unburnt carbon appears as black **soot**. In domestic fires, if there is an insufficient supply of oxygen to the fuel, carbon monoxide gas can be given off – this can lead to the death of the occupants due to the toxic effects of the gas.

Preparation of carbon dioxide

Carbon dioxide is prepared from calcium carbonate (marble chips) and hydrochloric acid using the same apparatus shown on page 116. The zinc is replaced by calcium carbonate (marble chips):

$CaCO_3 + 2HCl \rightarrow CaCl_2 + CO_2 + H_2O$

Carbon dioxide is collected over water because it has a low solubility in water.

Physical properties of carbon dioxide

Carbon dioxide is a colourless, odourless gas with a low solubility in water. It is denser than air and does not support combustion.

Chemical properties of carbon dioxide

1 Reaction with water

Carbon dioxide reacts with water to form the weak acid, carbonic acid, H_2CO_3:

$CO_2 + H_2O \rightarrow H_2CO_3$

The acid cannot be isolated from the solution and so is often simply written $CO_2(aq)$. Carbonic acid causes the acidity in fizzy drinks.

2 Reaction with burning magnesium

A piece of burning magnesium continues to burn in a gas jar of carbon dioxide.

Observations: A bright, white light; a white solid is produced (magnesium oxide) and there are black specks (carbon):

$2Mg + CO_2 \rightarrow 2MgO + C$

3 Reaction with an alkali

Carbon dioxide is an acidic oxide and it reacts with an alkali producing a salt and water. Carbon dioxide reacts with sodium hydroxide solution producing a colourless solution of the salt sodium carbonate and water.

$$CO_2 + 2NaOH \rightarrow Na_2CO_3 + H_2O$$

Test for carbon dioxide

Method: Bubble the gas through limewater.

Test result: The colourless solution becomes milky.

If carbon dioxide is bubbled through limewater until it is in excess, the colourless solution becomes milky (white precipitate is formed) and then the precipitate redissolves to form a colourless solution:

$$CO_2 + Ca(OH)_2 \rightarrow CaCO_3 + H_2O$$
      limewater   white ppt

$$CaCO_3 + CO_2 + H_2O \rightarrow Ca(HCO_3)_2$$
white ppt   colourless solution

Uses of carbon dioxide

● In fire extinguishers

● Making carbonated drinks

● As 'dry ice'.

Carbon dioxide is used in fire extinguishers because it does not support combustion – it is also denser than air and so covers the burning fuel.

Carbon dioxide is used in making carbonated drinks because it has a low solubility in water. When a bottle of a carbonated drink is opened, the gas is released with a fizz. It also gives the drink an acidic taste due to the carbonic acid present.

Solid carbon dioxide is called dry ice and it is used to produce fog effects on stage. This is because dry ice sublimes (changes from a solid to a gas) and causes the water vapour in the air to condense to form a fog.

Nitrogen

Revised

Physical properties

Nitrogen is a colourless, odourless gas that is insoluble in water.

● It is a diatomic gas, N_2.

● It is an unreactive gas. The lack of reactivity of nitrogen is because of the triple covalent bond between the nitrogen atoms in N_2 molecules. The triple covalent bond requires substantial energy to break before the nitrogen atoms can react.

Preparation of nitrogen

An impure sample of nitrogen is prepared in the laboratory by removing carbon dioxide, oxygen and water vapour from a sample of air.

● Carbon dioxide is removed by bubbling air through an alkaline solution, such as sodium hydroxide:

$$CO_2 + 2NaOH \rightarrow Na_2CO_3 + H_2O$$

● Oxygen is removed by passing the 'air' over heated copper, which reacts to form copper(II) oxide.

$$2Cu + O_2 \rightarrow 2CuO$$

● Finally the water vapour in the 'air' is removed by passing the remaining mixture of gases through concentrated sulfuric acid, which acts as a **dehydrating agent** removing the water vapour.

● The nitrogen produced is collected over water.

It is **impure** because it contains noble gases, such as argon. These gases do not interfere with the reactions of nitrogen because they are **inert gases**.

Chemical properties

Nitrogen is a relatively unreactive gas but it will react with burning magnesium to form magnesium nitride, Mg_3N_2. Even when magnesium burns in air, it forms about 10% magnesium nitride and 90% magnesium oxide.

In industry nitrogen and hydrogen react to form ammonia – this is the **Haber process**.

● Nitrogen and hydrogen are mixed in a 1:3 ratio. They are reacted at 450 °C, a pressure of 200 atm and with an iron catalyst.

$$N_2 + 3H_2 \rightleftharpoons 2NH_3$$

● The double arrow represents a **reversible reaction**. The forward reaction occurs where nitrogen and hydrogen are converted into ammonia, but some of the ammonia formed can then break down to form nitrogen and hydrogen. The reaction happens in both directions.

● Only about 10% of the nitrogen and hydrogen are converted to ammonia. The gases are cooled to condense the ammonia. The unreacted nitrogen and hydrogen are recycled.

● The Haber process cannot be demonstrated in the laboratory because of the high pressure and temperature used, the specialised plant required and safety of staff and students. It would also be too expensive.

● A lower temperature results in a higher yield of ammonia in this industrial process but the lower temperature would cause a lower rate of reaction. 450 °C is a compromise temperature between a reasonable rate of reaction and the yield obtained in a certain period of time.

- A higher pressure would result in a higher yield of ammonia but pressure is expensive to apply and thick-walled vessels are required to contain the pressure, which adds to the cost of the process. High pressures are also a greater safety risk for staff working on the site.

Uses of nitrogen

Nitrogen has two main uses:

- Liquid nitrogen is used as a coolant
- In food packaging nitrogen creates an inert atmosphere to keep food fresh.

Ammonia

Physical properties

Ammonia, NH_3, is a colourless, pungent gas that is soluble in water and less dense than air.

Test for ammonia

Method: Dip a glass rod in concentrated hydrochloric acid and put this in a sample of the gas.

Test result: If ammonia is present, a white 'smoke' of ammonium chloride is observed.

Ammonia gas reacts with hydrogen chloride gas forming ammonium chloride which appears as a white smoke or solid

$NH_3 + HCl \rightarrow NH_4Cl$

Detecting ammonium compounds

An ammonium compound can be detected in the laboratory by heating a solid thought to be an ammonium compound with a solid alkali metal hydroxide or alkaline earth metal hydroxide – e.g. sodium hydroxide or calcium hydroxide:

$NH_4Cl + NaOH \rightarrow NH_3 + NaCl + H_2O$

$2NH_4Cl + Ca(OH)_2 \rightarrow 2NH_3 + CaCl_2 + 2H_2O$

Any gas produced can be tested to see if it is ammonia. Only a solid ammonium compound will produce ammonia gas if heated with a solid Group 1 or 2 metal hydroxide. The most common solid Group 1 or 2 metal hydroxide used is sodium hydroxide, NaOH.

This reaction can be used to prepare and collect ammonia. The apparatus used is shown in the diagram on the right.

> **Exam tip**
>
> Ammonia is often confused with 'ammonium'. Ammonia is a compound (NH_3) but 'ammonium' is an ion with the formula NH_4^+. Remember that any chemical with 'ammonium' as part of its name must contain NH_4 – ammonia is simply NH_3.

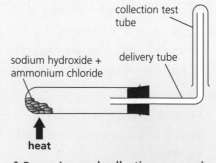

↑ **Preparing and collecting ammonia**

collection test tube

delivery tube

sodium hydroxide + ammonium chloride

heat

Chemical properties

1   Ammonia is basic – it forms an alkaline solution because of the formation of ammonium hydroxide, which produces **hydroxide ions** in water. A solution of ammonia in water is called aqueous ammonia and it is a weak alkali (page 62).

$$NH_3 + H_2O \rightarrow NH_4^+ + OH^-$$

2   Ammonia reacts with dilute mineral acids to form ammonium salts. Ammonium sulfate and ammonium nitrate are commonly used artificial fertilisers. They are called **nitrogenous fertilisers**:

$$NH_3 + HCl \rightarrow NH_4Cl \text{ (ammonium chloride)}$$

$$2NH_3 + H_2SO_4 \rightarrow (NH_4)_2SO_4 \text{ (ammonium sulfate)}$$

$$NH_3 + HNO_3 \rightarrow NH_4NO_3 \text{ (ammonium nitrate)}$$

There can be environmental problems with nitrogenous fertilisers. Excessive use of nitrogenous fertilisers on soil leads to **leaching** of nitrates into soil water and finally into river water. This leads to an environmental problem called **eutrophication**.

- Excessive use of nitrogenous fertilisers may also cause increased levels of nitrates in drinking water from reservoirs.

- These increased levels of nitrates have been linked to stomach cancer and also blue-baby syndrome.

- However, without artificial fertilisers, there would not be enough food produced for the human race to survive.

- Plants require nitrogen for growth and this is provided by nitrogenous fertilisers making plants grow faster and larger – this leads to a higher crop yield and bigger profits.

- All nitrates are soluble in water, which makes nitrate compounds difficult to remove from water.

Using aqueous ammonia to test for metal ions in solution

Aqueous ammonia (a solution of ammonia in water) can be used to test for the presence of metal ions in solution.

- Aqueous ammonia contains hydroxide ions.

- Most metal hydroxides are insoluble in water.

- The addition of hydroxide ions (OH^-) to a solution containing certain metal ions will produce a precipitate.

Note: *For Double Award Chemistry you need to know that ammonia is used in the manufacture of nitric acid, explosives and ammonia.*

Exam tip

You need to be able to recognise the process of eutrophication and to explain it. The answer given below explains the process and covers all the points the examiners want to see:

- Nitrogenous fertilisers in rivers and lakes leads to excess algae growth.

- This leads to death of algae.

- Decomposing microorganisms use up oxygen gas in the water breaking down dead algae.

- This leads to a lack of oxygen in the water and the death of fish.

Copper(II) ions, Cu^{2+}

- Aqueous ammonia is added to a solution containing copper(II) ions.
- A **pale blue precipitate** of copper(II) hydroxide is formed.

$$Cu^{2+}(aq) + 2OH^-(aq) \rightarrow Cu(OH)_2(s)$$
$$\text{pale blue precipitate}$$

- On addition of excess aqueous ammonia, the precipitate redissolves to form a **dark blue solution**.

Iron(II) ions, Fe^{2+}

- Aqueous ammonia is added to a solution containing iron(II) ions.
- A **pale green precipitate** of iron(II) hydroxide is formed.

$$Fe^{2+}(aq) + 2OH^-(aq) \rightarrow Fe(OH)_2(s)$$
$$\text{pale green precipitate}$$

- On addition of excess aqueous ammonia, the precipitate does not redissolve.

Iron(III) ions, Fe^{3+}

- Aqueous ammonia is added to a solution containing iron(III) ions.
- A **red-brown precipitate** of iron(III) hydroxide is formed.

$$Fe^{3+}(aq) + 3OH^-(aq) \rightarrow Fe(OH)_3(s)$$
$$\text{red-brown precipitate}$$

- On addition of excess aqueous ammonia, the precipitate does not redissolve.

Aluminium ions, Al^{3+}

- Aqueous ammonia is added to a solution containing aluminium ions.
- A **white precipitate** of aluminium hydroxide is formed.
- $Al^{3+}(aq) + 3OH^-(aq) \rightarrow Al(OH)_3(s)$

$$\text{white precipitate}$$

- On addition of excess aqueous ammonia, the precipitate does not redissolve.

Zinc ions, Zn^{2+}

- Aqueous ammonia is added to a solution containing zinc ions.
- A **white precipitate** of zinc hydroxide is formed.
- $Zn^{2+}(aq) + 2OH^-(aq) \rightarrow Zn(OH)_2(s)$

$$\text{white precipitate}$$

- On addition of excess aqueous ammonia, the precipitate redissolves to form a colourless solution.

Magnesium ions, Mg^{2+}

- Aqueous ammonia is added to a solution containing magnesium ions.
- A **white precipitate** of magnesium hydroxide is formed.

$$Mg^{2+}(aq) + 2OH^-(aq) \rightarrow Mg(OH)_2(s)$$
$$\text{white precipitate}$$

- On addition of excess aqueous ammonia, the precipitate does not redissolve.

Physical properties of oxygen

Oxygen is a colourless, odourless gas that is only slightly soluble in water and is slightly denser than air. Oxygen is diatomic, O_2.

Laboratory preparation of oxygen

Oxygen is made using hydrogen peroxide and manganese(IV) oxide using the same apparatus shown on page 116. The zinc is replaced by manganese(IV) oxide and the hydrochloric acid by hydrogen peroxide. Manganese (IV) oxide is also called manganese dioxide – it is a catalyst (see page 111) used to speed up the decomposition of hydrogen peroxide:

$$2H_2O_2 \rightarrow 2H_2O + O_2$$

Test for oxygen

Method: Apply a glowing splint.

Test result: The glowing splint relights.

Uses of oxygen

● In medicine
● In welding
● In rocket engines
● In steel making.

Chemical properties of oxygen

1   Reaction with hydrogen

    Observations: Hydrogen burns with a clean, blue flame producing a colourless, odourless gas that condenses to form a colourless liquid which is water.

    $$2H_2 + O_2 \rightarrow 2H_2O$$

2   Reaction with carbon

    Observations: Black carbon burns with an orange, sooty flame forming a colourless gas, carbon dioxide.

    $$C + O_2 \rightarrow CO_2$$

    If there is a limited supply of oxygen, the combustion reaction produces carbon monoxide.

    $$2C + O_2 \rightarrow 2CO$$

3   Reaction with sulfur

    Observations: Yellow, solid sulfur melts to a red liquid and burns with a blue flame giving a colourless pungent gas, sulfur dioxide.

    $$S + O_2 \rightarrow SO_2$$

4 Reaction with magnesium

Observations: Grey, solid magnesium burns with a bright, white light, releasing heat and producing a white solid, magnesium oxide.

$2Mg + O_2 \rightarrow 2MgO$

5 Reaction with zinc

Observations: Grey, solid zinc glows red on heating with oxygen producing a yellow solid, which changes to a white solid on cooling, zinc oxide.

$2Zn + O_2 \rightarrow 2ZnO$

Note: *Zinc oxide is normally a white solid but it is yellow when heated.*

6 Reaction with iron

Observations: Grey, solid iron filings burn with orange sparks producing a black solid, Fe_3O_4.

$3Fe + 2O_2 \rightarrow Fe_3O_4$

7 Reaction with copper

Observations: Red/pink solid glows and forms a black solid, copper oxide.

$2Cu + O_2 \rightarrow 2CuO$

Sulfur

Revised

Physical properties of sulfur

Sulfur is a brittle, yellow solid.

Allotropy of sulfur

Sulfur exists as three allotropes:

● rhombic sulfur

● monoclinic sulfur

● plastic sulfur

Allotropes are different forms of the same element in the same physical state (page 28).

Chemical properties of sulfur

1 Combustion of sulfur

Observations: Yellow sulfur melts to a red liquid and burns with a blue flame in air/oxygen producing a colourless pungent gas.

$S + O_2 \rightarrow SO_2$

2 Reaction of sulfur with iron

Observations: The mixture of solid, yellow sulfur and grey, solid iron glows red when heated, forming a black solid.

$Fe + S \rightarrow FeS$

This reaction is often used to show that the product of a chemical reaction is different from the reactants. Iron(II) sulfide is a non-magnetic, black solid, whereas the reactants are a magnetic, grey solid and a yellow, non-magnetic solid. In a chemical reaction you cannot predict the properties of the new material formed.

Physical properties of sulfur dioxide

Sulfur dioxide is a colourless, pungent gas that is soluble in water and denser than air.

Chemical properties of sulfur dioxide

1 Sulfur dioxide reacts with water to form the weak acid sulfurous acid, H_2SO_3.

$$SO_2 + H_2O \rightarrow H_2SO_3$$

Sulfurous acid forms salts called **sulfites** – the sulfite ion is SO_3^{2-}.

- Many fossil fuels contain sulfur impurities that burn on combustion to form sulfur dioxide, which is released into the atmosphere.
- Sulfur dioxide in the atmosphere reacts with rain water to form the weak acid **sulfurous acid** – this causes **acid rain**.
- **Acid rain** has three main effects:
  - it corrodes limestone buildings and statues
  - it defoliates trees
  - it pollutes lakes and rivers killing fish.
- **Acid rain** can be minimised by:
  - removing sulfur from fossil fuels before burning
  - using renewable energy resources
  - removing sulfur dioxide from factory/power station emissions
  - using cars fitted with catalytic converters
  - burning less fossil fuels.

2 Sulfur dioxide is an acidic oxide and reacts with alkalis forming sulfite salts and water.

$$SO_2 + 2NaOH \rightarrow Na_2SO_3 + H_2O$$
$$\text{sodium}$$
$$\text{sulfite}$$

The industrial manufacture of sulfuric acid

Sulfuric acid is manufactured from sulfur in the **Contact process**. There are four main stages of production:

Stage 1: Combustion of sulfur

Sulfur is burned in air to form sulfur dioxide.

$$S + O_2 \rightarrow SO_2$$

Stage 2: Catalytic production of sulfur trioxide

The sulfur dioxide is mixed with more air and at a temperature of 450 °C, a pressure of 2 atmospheres and in the presence of a vanadium(V) oxide, V_2O_5, catalyst. Under these conditions the sulfur dioxide is converted to sulfur trioxide.

$$2SO_2 + O_2 \rightleftharpoons 2SO_3$$

Stage 3: Absorption in concentrated sulfuric acid

The sulfur trioxide is dissolved in concentrated sulfuric acid to form oleum, $H_2S_2O_7$.

$$SO_3 + H_2SO_4 \rightarrow H_2S_2O_7$$

Stage 4: Dilution of oleum

The oleum is mixed with water to produce **concentrated sulfuric acid**.

$$H_2S_2O_7 + H_2O \rightarrow 2H_2SO_4$$

Sulfur trioxide is not mixed directly with water because the reaction is too **exothermic** and produces a corrosive mist which is difficult to contain.

Note: *Stage 2 is a reversible reaction.*

● In stage 2, a lower temperature would result in a higher yield of sulfur trioxide but the lower temperature would cause a lower rate of reaction.

● 450 °C is a 'compromise temperature' between a reasonable rate of reaction and the yield obtained in a certain period of time.

● A higher pressure would result in a higher yield of sulfur trioxide but pressure is expensive to apply and thick-walled vessels are needed to contain the pressure, which adds to the cost of the process. Also higher pressures are a greater safety risk for staff working on the site.

Chemical properties of dilute sulfuric acid

Dilute sulfuric acid is a typical acid reacting with metals, metal oxides, metal hydroxides, metal carbonates and ammonia.

1 Reaction with metals.

$$Mg + H_2SO_4 \rightarrow MgSO_4 + H_2$$

2 Reaction with metal oxides.

$$MgO + H_2SO_4 \rightarrow MgSO_4 + H_2O$$

3 Reaction with metal hydroxides.

$$Mg(OH)_2 + H_2SO_4 \rightarrow MgSO_4 + 2H_2O$$

4 Reaction with metal carbonates.

$$MgCO_3 + H_2SO_4 \rightarrow MgSO_4 + CO_2 + H_2O$$

5 Reaction with ammonia.

$$2NH_3 + H_2SO_4 \rightarrow (NH_4)_2SO_4$$

Uses of sulfuric acid

● In car batteries

● In the manufacture of fertilisers.

Exam tip

You must be able to write balanced symbol equations and state the observations for the reactions of any metal, metal oxide, metal hydroxide or metal carbonate with sulfuric acid. Remember that the sulfate ion is SO_4^{2-} and has a valency of 2.

● Sulfuric acid forms sulfate salts, most of which are soluble in water.

● All Group 1 and 2 sulfate salts are white and form colourless solutions.

Note: *Barium sulfate is insoluble in water.*

Chemical properties of concentrated sulfuric acid

1 Reaction of concentrated sulfuric acid with sugar (sucrose)

Concentrated sulfuric acid **dehydrates** sugar to form carbon, which is a black solid, and water, which is released as water vapour.

Observations: The reaction does not start immediately. The sugar swells up and rises in the container. Heat is released and there is a distinct caramel smell together with a pungent odour. A black solid is formed.

2 Reaction of concentrated sulfuric acid with hydrated copper(II) sulfate, $CuSO_4.5H_2O$

Observations: The blue solid changes to white.

The concentrated sulfuric acid again behaves as a dehydrating agent removing the water of crystallisation forming the white solid anhydrous copper(II) sulfate, $CuSO_4$.

Concentrated sulfuric acid acts as a **dehydrating agent**.

Diluting concentrated sulfuric acid

When diluting concentrated sulfuric acid, a large amount of heat is evolved – so the acid must be diluted slowly with stirring to prevent too much heat being produced too quickly. Concentrated sulfuric acid is corrosive.

- Safety glasses and gloves should be worn.
- The concentrated acid should be added to a large volume of water, slowly with stirring. Water **must never** be added to a concentrated acid.

1 In each case, name two chemicals needed to prepare these gases:

   a) oxygen; **b)** carbon dioxide; **c)** hydrogen; **d)** ammonia   [8]

2 State how you would carry out the test for the following gases and what you would observe if the gas was present:

   a) hydrogen **[2]**; **b)** carbon dioxide **[3]**; **c)** oxygen **[2]**; **d)** ammonia **[4]**

3 Explain, using an equation, why a solution of ammonia is alkaline.   [3]

4 State two uses of carbon dioxide.   [2]

5 What is observed when a solution of ammonia is added slowly until it is in excess to a solution containing copper(II) ions?   [4]

6 In the industrial production of sulfuric acid:

   a) Name the starting materials.   [2]

   b) Name the catalyst used in the second stage.   [1]

   c) What operating temperature is used in the second stage?   [1]

7 What name is given to the industrial process for the production of sulfuric acid?   [1]

8 Describe how you would **safely** dilute a sample of concentrated sulfuric acid.   [3]

9 What is observed when some concentrated sulfuric acid is added to hydrated copper(II) sulfate?   [2]

10 Sulfur burns in air:

   a) Write a balanced symbol equation for sulfur burning in air.   [2]

   b) What is observed when sulfur burns in air?   [3]

11 Carbon dioxide reacts with burning magnesium:

   a) Write a balanced symbol equation for the reaction.   [3]

   b) What is observed during this reaction?   [3]

12 Write a balanced symbol equation for the production of ammonia in the Haber process.   [3]

13 What is observed when solid potassium carbonate reacts with dilute sulfuric acid?   [3]

14 What is meant by the term 'allotrope'?   [2]

15 State the names of the three allotropes of sulfur.   [3]

Go online for the answers   Online

14 Organic Chemistry

Fossil fuels and living things are based on the element **carbon**. Organic chemicals are obtained from crude oil.

Crude oil is a black, viscous liquid and it is a mixture of **hydrocarbons** – compounds containing only hydrogen and carbon. Some of these hydrocarbons are solids and gases dissolved in the liquid.

Exam tip

The definition of a hydrocarbon is a very common question. The key points are that a hydrocarbon is a *compound* containing *only carbon and hydrogen*.

Fossil fuels
Revised ▢

Fossil fuels are formed from dead plants and animals over millions of years under the action of heat and pressure. Examples of fossil fuels are natural gas, LPG, petrol, diesel, paraffin, candle wax, peat, lignite, coal and coke.

● Fossil fuels are non-renewable resources.

● Non-renewable resources are those that cannot be replaced in a human lifetime and will eventually run out.

● A renewable resource is one that can be replaced in a human lifetime. Important renewable resources include biomass – for example, wood from trees.

Spillage of crude oil causes the following environmental problems:

● it destroys habitats

● it harms diving birds

● it creates eyesores on beaches and shorelines.

Fractional distillation of crude oil
Revised ▢

Fractional distillation separates crude oil into simpler mixtures of hydrocarbons called fractions. Fractional distillation is carried out in a fractionating column.

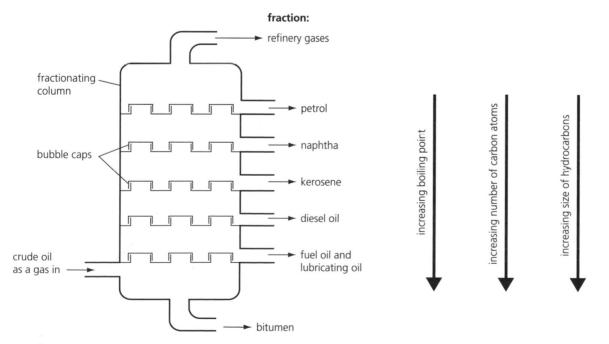

↑ **A fractionating column is used to separate crude oil into fractions**

- The crude oil enters at the bottom as a hot gaseous mixture.
- The fractionating column has bubble caps, which allow gases to move upwards.
- The temperature decreases *up* the column.
- As the gases move up the column, hydrocarbons condense when the temperature of the column is the same as their boiling point.

The table below shows the major fractions obtained from crude oil in order of increasing size of molecules and increasing boiling point, along with some of their uses.

Uses of some fractions from crude oil

Fraction	Use
Refinery gases	Bottled gases
Petrol	Vehicle fuel
Naphtha	Chemicals and plastics
Kerosene	Aircraft fuel
Diesel oil	Large vehicle fuel
Fuel oil and lubricating oil	Fuel for ships Lubricants
Bitumen	Road tar

Homologous series of organic compounds

A **homologous series** is a family of organic compounds that have the same general formula, show similar chemical properties, show a gradation in their physical properties and differ by a CH_2 unit.

There are four homologous series required for GCSE Chemistry – alkanes, alkenes, alcohols and carboxylic acids.

- **Alkanes** are relatively unreactive hydrocarbons.
- **Alkenes** are more reactive hydrocarbons.
- **Alcohols** and **carboxylic acids** are not hydrocarbons because they contain oxygen atoms as well as carbon and hydrogen atoms. Alcohols and carboxylic acids are reactive organic compounds.

General formula for a homologous series

A general formula is a one involving a variable number, *n*, which allows the molecular formula of any compound in a particular homologous series to be determined.

- The general formula of the alkanes is C_nH_{2n+2}. If $n = 3$ then the formula of the alkane with three carbon atoms is $C_3H_{(2\times3 + 2)} = C_3H_8$. This is the molecular formula of propane.
- For organic compounds containing one carbon atom, the prefix **meth-** is used.
- For organic compound containing two carbon atoms, the prefix **eth-** is used. For three carbon atoms **prop-** is used, and for four carbon atoms **but-** is used.

The table below gives the general formulae for the four homologous series studied at this level.

Formulae of some organic compounds

Homologous series	General formula	Values of n required
Alkanes	C_nH_{2n+2}	1, 2, 3 and 4
Alkenes	C_nH_{2n}	2 and 3
Alcohols	$C_nH_{2n+1}OH$	1 and 2
Carboxylic acids	$C_nH_{2n+1}COOH$	0 and 1

Alkanes

Revised ☐

The table below names the first four alkanes with their molecular formula, structural formula and state at room temperature and pressure.

n	Name	Molecular formula	Structural formula	State at room temperature and pressure
1	Methane	CH_4	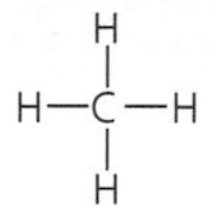 H—C—H (with H above and below)	Gas
2	Ethane	C_2H_6	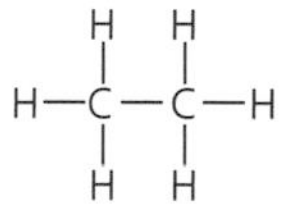 H—C—C—H	Gas
3	Propane	C_3H_8	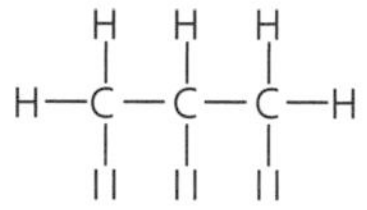 H—C—C—C—H	Gas
4	Butane	C_4H_{10}	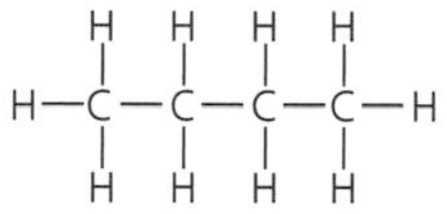 H—C—C—C—C—H	Gas

↑ The first four alkanes

Alkenes

Revised ☐

The table below names the first two alkenes with their molecular formula, structural formula and state at room temperature and pressure.

n	Name	Molecular formula	Structural formula	State at room temperature and pressure
2	Ethene	C_2H_4	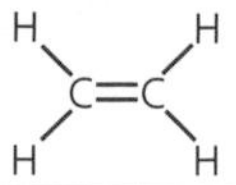 C=C	Gas
3	Propene	C_3H_6	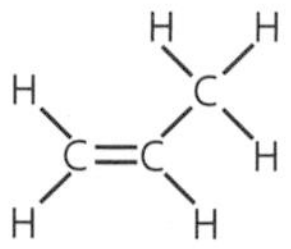 C=C	Gas

↑ The first two alkenes

Alcohols

The table below names the first two alcohols with their molecular formula, structural formula and state at room temperature and pressure.

n	Name	Molecular formula	Structural formula	State at room temperature and pressure
1	Methanol	CH_3OH	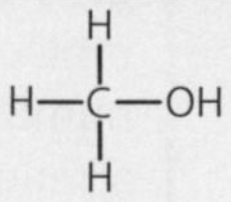	Liquid
2	Ethanol	C_2H_5OH	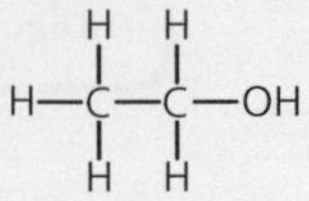	Liquid

↑ The first two alcohols

Carboxylic acids

The table below names the first two carboxylic acids with their molecular formula, structural formula and state at room temperature and pressure.

n	Name	Molecular formula	Structural formula	State at room temperature and pressure
0	Methanoic acid	HCOOH	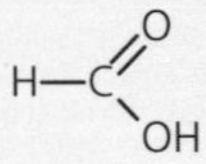	Liquid
1	Ethanoic acid	CH_3COOH	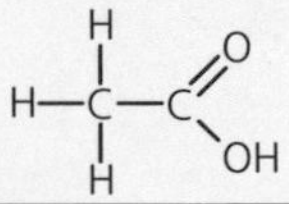	Liquid

↑ The first two carboxylic acids

Note: *Many organic compounds have a **functional group**. A functional group is a reactive group that causes many of the reactions of the compounds in the homologous series.*

Alkanes do not have a functional group. Alkanes are a less reactive homologous series because they don't have a functional group. However, they do undergo combustion. Natural gas is mainly methane and bottled gas is a mixture of propane and butane.

- The functional group of alkenes is C=C

- The functional group of alcohols is —OH

- The functional group of carboxylic acids is

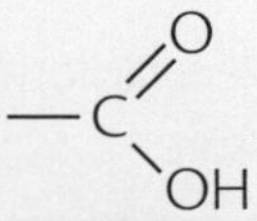

- n in a general formula often represents the number of carbon atoms in molecules – this is true for alkanes, alkenes and alcohols. However, the functional group of a carboxylic acid contains a carbon atom, so the values of n start at 0.

Exam tip

Normally when a question asks for the structure of an alcohol or a carboxylic acid, it is enough to show the functional group as –OH (worth 1 mark). But if the question asks for all bonds to be shown then show the bond between the O and H atom (–O–H). This would be worth 2 marks.

Combustion of organic compounds

Combustion is the reaction of a fuel with oxygen producing oxides and releasing heat.

The higher the percentage carbon content of an organic compound, the more orange the flame with which it burns in air. A lower percentage carbon content causes the flame to be blue as opposed to orange.

Complete combustion happens when a fuel burns in a plentiful supply of oxygen/air to form carbon dioxide and water and releasing heat. For example:

$CH_4 + 2O_2 \rightarrow CO_2 + 2H_2O$

$2C_2H_6 + 7O_2 \rightarrow 4CO_2 + 6H_2O$

Incomplete combustion happens when a fuel burns in a limited supply of oxygen/air to form carbon monoxide, and sometimes soot (carbon), and water and releasing heat. For example:

$C_2H_4 + 2O_2 \rightarrow 2CO + 2H_2O$

$2C_3H_8 + 7O_2 \rightarrow 6CO + 8H_2O$

Carbon monoxide is a poisonous gas (see page 117).

> **Exam tip**
>
> Equations for combustion are common in organic questions. Equations are not required for the production of soot, but you may be asked to write a balanced symbol equation for incomplete combustion forming carbon monoxide and water.

Balancing equations for combustion of hydrocarbons

To balance a complete combustion equation:

1 The number of carbon atoms in the hydrocarbon and the balancing number in front of the CO_2 are the same.

2 The number of hydrogen atoms in the hydrocarbon is divided by 2 to get the number in front of the H_2O.

3 Count the *total number of oxygen atoms* in the CO_2 (remember CO_2 has 2) and the H_2O and divide by 2 to get the number in front of O_2.

4 If the number in front of O_2 has a half (e.g. 2½) multiply all the balancing numbers by 2 to get whole numbers.

> **Exam tip**
>
> If you are balancing an incomplete combustion equation, replace carbon dioxide with carbon monoxide in step 1 and step 3. Remember that carbon monoxide, CO, has only one oxygen atom per molecule.

Combustion of alcohols

Alcohols also undergo combustion. Alcohols have a lower percentage carbon content than alkanes or alkenes and so burn with a blue flame (sometimes with an orange tip). Alcohols normally undergo complete combustion, but in a very limited supply of oxygen carbon monoxide and even soot (carbon) may be formed.

Here are the word equations and balanced symbol equations for complete combustion:

● methanol + oxygen → carbon dioxide + water

$2CH_3OH + 3O_2 \rightarrow 2CO_2 + 4H_2O$

● ethanol + oxygen → carbon dioxide + water

$C_2H_5OH + 3O_2 \rightarrow 2CO_2 + 3H_2O$

... and for incomplete combustion:

● ethanol + oxygen → carbon monoxide + water

$C_2H_5OH + 2O_2 \rightarrow 2CO + 3H_2O$

> **Exam tip**
>
> Balancing the equations for the combustion of alcohols follows the same process given for hydrocarbons – but remember to take the oxygen atom in the alcohol into account when counting the total oxygen atoms on both sides of the equation in step 3.

Testing the products of combustion

The main products of combustion are carbon dioxide and water vapour. The presence of these two products can be detected using two chemical tests:

● Cool the gases and a colourless liquid will condense – add this liquid to anhydrous copper(II) sulfate, any water present will change the anhydrous copper(II) sulfate from white to blue.

● Bubble the gases through limewater – any carbon dioxide present changes the limewater from colourless to milky.

Atmospheric pollution due to combustion of hydrocarbon fuels

Greenhouse effect

Burning hydrocarbon fuels for heat and for the production of electrical energy leads to increased levels of gases such as carbon dioxide and sulfur dioxide in the atmosphere. These gases are considered to be polluting because they cause adverse environmental problems.

Scientists think that increased levels of carbon dioxide in the atmosphere are leading to the greenhouse effect, which causes:

● global warming
● rising sea levels
● melting of the polar ice caps
● climate change.

The greenhouse effect may be minimised by:

● using alternative energy resources such as wind, tidal, solar, wave, hydroelectric and nuclear power

● using clean fuels such as hydrogen

● using 'cleaner fuels' such as ethanol.

Acid rain

Fossil fuels often contain sulfur impurities. When the fossil fuel burns, the sulfur reacts to form sulfur dioxide.

$S + O_2 \rightarrow SO_2$

Sulfur dioxide is an acidic gas that dissolves in rainwater forming sulfurous acid:

$SO_2 + H_2O \rightarrow H_2SO_3$

Rain containing sulfurous acid falls as acid rain, which has several effects:

● it defoliates trees
● it pollutes rivers and lakes killing fish
● it destroys limestone statues, buildings and natural limestone features.

Acid rain may be minimised by:

● burning less fossil fuels

● removing sulfur from fuels

● treating emissions from factories and power stations to remove sulfur dioxide

● using catalytic converters in car exhaust systems.

Chemistry of alkanes

Revised ☐

Alkanes are relatively unreactive organic molecules. They do undergo combustion (page 133)

Chemistry of alkenes

Revised ☐

Combustion of an alkene

Observations: Alkenes burn with an orange flame releasing heat and producing colourless gases. For example:

$$C_2H_4 + 3O_2 \rightarrow 2CO_2 + 2H_2O$$

Saturation and unsaturation

Alkenes have one C=C double bond per molecule – they are **unsaturated**.

Alkanes have no C=C double bonds – they are **saturated**.

The test for a C=C double bond or unsaturation is to add the substance to bromine water and mix well. An unsaturated substance/any alkene will cause a colour change from red-brown to colourless; a saturated substance/any alkane will cause no change.

Note: *Alcohols and carboxylic acids do not contain the C=C functional group and so are saturated – when added to bromine water the colour will remain red-brown. Bromine water is often used to distinguish between alkanes and alkenes.*

Formation of ethanol from ethene

Ethene reacts with steam producing ethanol:

$$C_2H_4 + H_2O \rightarrow C_2H_5OH$$

Addition polymerisation

Polymerisation is the process of creating a long molecule from small molecules which form the repeating unit in the **polymer**.

Addition polymerisation is the process of adding molecules together to form a polymer as the only product – the long molecule is the polymer.

- The simple molecule from which a polymer is formed is called the **monomer**.
- The monomer has a C=C double bond.
- The monomer is an **alkene**.

- The polymer is shown as the monomer with only a single bond in a square bracket.
- 'n' molecules of monomer must be at the beginning of the equation.
- The polymer structure has 'n' after it to show that the polymer repeats n times.

The diagram below shows the general equation for addition polymerisation.

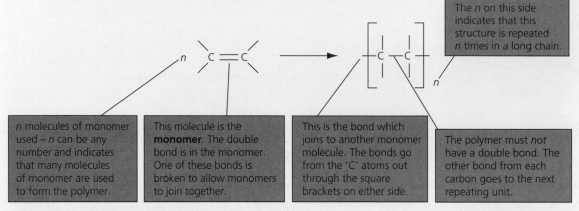

The *n* on this side indicates that this structure is repeated *n* times in a long chain.

n molecules of monomer used – *n* can be any number and indicates that many molecules of monomer are used to form the polymer.

This molecule is the **monomer**. The double bond is in the monomer. One of these bonds is broken to allow monomers to join together.

This is the bond which joins to another monomer molecule. The bonds go from the 'C' atoms out through the square brackets on either side.

The polymer must *not* have a double bond. The other bond from each carbon goes to the next repeating unit.

↑ **The general equation for addition polymerisation**

Two common addition polymers are:

- polythene

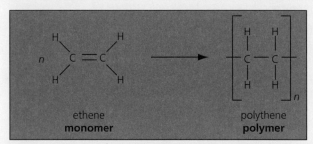

ethene
monomer

polythene
polymer

- poly vinyl chloride (PVC)

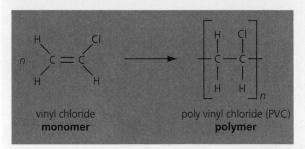

vinyl chloride
monomer

poly vinyl chloride (PVC)
polymer

Uses of polymers

The uses of any material depend on its properties.

- Polythene is used for plastic bags and bottles because it can be coloured and moulded, and it is flexible.

- PVC is used for door and window frames because it can also be coloured and moulded, but it is more durable than polythene.

Polymers have replaced many traditional materials because they are cheaper, lighter and less likely to rot, corrode or rust. For example, PVC is used for window and door frames instead of wood; many parts of a car body are made from polymers instead of metals.

Disposal of polymers

Addition polymers are non-biodegradable, which means they cannot be broken down in the environment. There are two methods of disposal of polymers – landfill and incineration.

The table below shows the advantages and disadvantages associated with each method of disposal.

Comparing methods of disposal of polymers

Method of disposal of polymers	Advantages	Disadvantages
Landfill	• Local treatment of waste so less transport of waste needed • Land can be re-landscaped after use	• Wastes land • Polluting gases released
Incineration	• Less waste going to landfill • Heat energy can be harnessed to generate electricity	• Ash residue is toxic and specialised landfill needed • Polluting gases released

Chemistry of alcohols

Revised

Combustion

Observations: Methanol and ethanol burn with a clean blue flame and heat is released. For example:

$$C_2H_5OH + 3O_2 \rightarrow 2CO_2 + 3H_2O$$

Fermentation

Ethanol can be produced by **fermentation** of sugars. Sugar solution is mixed with yeast in warm conditions in the absence of oxygen. The reaction produces carbon dioxide and ethanol.

Fermentation can produce a solution of ethanol in water of approximately 12–15%. This concentration of ethanol kills the yeast, so a higher concentration is not possible simply by fermentation.

A more concentrated solution of ethanol, for example those in spirits like vodka and rum, can be produced from this solution by fractional distillation.

Ethanol is present in alcoholic drinks – these can impair judgement and can cause damage to the brain and the liver. Ethanol can be detected in a sample of breath using infrared spectroscopy in the 'breathalyser' test.

Oxidation by air

Ethanol in alcoholic drinks can be oxidised to ethanoic acid over time by the oxygen in air. Ethanoic acid is the acid present in vinegar, and this acid is what makes wine go sour if a bottle is left open and not consumed.

Oxidation by acidified potassium dichromate solution

Potassium dichromate ($K_2Cr_2O_7$) is a common oxidising agent used in organic chemistry. It is an orange solid that is soluble in water. A solution of it is acidified using dilute sulfuric acid to form 'acidified potassium dichromate solution' – this solution is also orange.

Methanol and ethanol both react with acidified potassium dichromate solution. This is usually carried out in a test tube with the alcohol mixed with the acidified potassium dichromate solution. The test tube is then placed in a beaker of warm water. A colour change from orange to green is observed.

From the organic compounds in this course, only methanol and ethanol will show this colour change with acidified potassium dichromate solution. This is a test for these two alcohols.

Ethanol is used as a solvent, as a fuel and in alcoholic drinks.

Chemistry of carboxylic acids
Revised ☐

Note: *The definition of a weak acid is not required in Double Award Chemistry.*

Carboxylic acids are weak acids because they are only partially ionised in water. Methanoic acid forms methanoate salts – the methanoate ion is $HCOO^-$. Ethanoic acid forms ethanoate salts – the ethanoate ion is CH_3COO^-.

A dilute solution of ethanoic acid is used as vinegar to flavour food.

Reaction with sodium carbonate

Observations: Bubbles of gas are formed, the solid disappears and a colourless solution is formed:

carboxylic acid + sodium carbonate → sodium salt + water + carbon dioxide

$$2CH_3COOH + Na_2CO_3 \rightarrow 2CH_3COONa + H_2O + CO_2$$
sodium
ethanoate

Of the organic compounds in this course, only carboxylic acids will release carbon dioxide when sodium carbonate is added to a sample. This is a way of distinguishing a carboxylic acid from other organic compounds. The gas can be identified as carbon dioxide by bubbling it through limewater, which changes from colourless to milky if carbon dioxide is present (page 118).

> **Exam tip**
>
> In the formula of the salt, 'methanoate' or 'ethanoate' is usually written first, for example, magnesium methanoate is $(HCOO)_2Mg$. However, it is acceptable to write it the other way round as $Mg(HCOO)_2$.

Reaction with magnesium

Observations: Bubbles of a gas are produced, heat is released, the metal disappears and a colourless solution is formed:

carboxylic acid + magnesium $\rightarrow$ magnesium salt + hydrogen

$2CH_3COOH + Mg \rightarrow (CH_3COO)_2Mg + H_2$

magnesium
ethanoate

The gas can be tested with a lit splint – it should pop if it is hydrogen.

Reaction with sodium hydroxide

Observations: Heat is released and the solution remains colourless:

General equation: carboxylic acid + sodium hydroxide $\rightarrow$ sodium salt + water

$HCOOH + NaOH \rightarrow HCOONa + H_2O$

sodium
methanoate

Properties of organic compounds

Revised

- The first four alkanes (CH_4, C_2H_6, C_3H_8 and C_4H_{10}) are colourless gases.
- The first two alkenes (C_2H_4, C_3H_6) are colourless gases.
- All polymers are white solids – coloured dyes can be added to make coloured plastics.
- Methanol and ethanol are colourless liquids with an alcohol-like smell.
- Methanoic acid is a colourless liquid with a pungent odour.
- Ethanoic acid is a colourless liquid with a vinegar-like smell.
- Methanol, ethanol, methanoic acid and ethanoic acid all mix with water.
- The higher the carbon content of an organic compound, the sootier (and more orange) the flame will be when it burns.
- The lower the carbon content of an organic compound, the less sooty (and more clean and blue) the flame will be when it burns.
- Alcohols burn with a cleaner, blue flame than the alkanes or alkenes.

Unknown organic compounds

Revised

You may be given information about an organic compound and have to identify it – or at least say which homologous series it belongs to – from the physical and chemical properties provided.

The table on page 140 summarises the chemical tests used to identify different homologous series. Other information may be given, such as melting point and boiling point, which allows you to determine a compound's state at room temperature and pressure, as well as the colour of its flame during combustion – an orange flame would indicate an alkane or alkene; a clean, blue flame would usually indicate an alcohol. Carboxylic acids do not burn easily.

Tests to identify different types of organic compounds

Organic compound	Alkane	Alkene	Alcohol	Carboxylic acid
Reaction with bromine water	Remains red-brown	Changes from red-brown to colourless	Remains red-brown	Remains red-brown
Reaction when warmed with acidified potassium dichromate solution	Solution remains orange	Solution remains orange	Solution changes from orange to green	Solution remains orange
Reaction with sodium carbonate	No reaction	No reaction	No reaction	Gas produced

Example 1

A colourless organic compound has a melting point of $-114\,°C$ and a boiling point of $79\,°C$. When a sample is burned on a watch glass, a clean blue flame is observed. When a sample is warmed with acidified potassium dichromate solution, the solution changes from orange to green. To which homologous series does the compound belong?

● The compound is a liquid at room temperature (based on its melting and boiling points) so it is an alcohol or a carboxylic acid.

● The clean, blue flame indicates a lower carbon content and suggests an alcohol because carboxylic acids do not burn easily.

● The key piece of evidence is the reaction with acidified potassium dichromate solution which indicates an **alcohol**.

Example 2

A gaseous hydrocarbon is bubbled through bromine water and the bromine water changes from red-brown to colourless. Identify the homologous series to which the hydrocarbon belongs.

● Bromine water is decolourised when it reacts with C=C double bonds.

● Alkenes contain C=C double bonds – the unknown hydrocarbon is an **alkene**.

1 Write molecular formulae for these organic substances:

a) ethane; **b)** ethene; **c)** butane; **d)** methane [4]

2 What is observed when ethene is bubbled through bromine water? [2]

3 What is meant by the term hydrocarbon? [2]

4 Name these molecules:

a) (structure)   **b)** (structure)   **c)** (structure) [3]

5 Write an equation for the complete combustion of ethanol. [3]

6 What is produced when ethene reacts with steam? [1]

7 What process is used to separate the hydrocarbons in crude oil? [2]

8 What would be observed when ethanol is warmed with acidified potassium dichromate solution? [2]

9 Write an equation for the reaction of magnesium with ethanoic acid. [3]

10 What is meant by the term 'homologous series'? [3]

11 Name these polymers:

a) (structure)   **b)** (structure) [2]

12 State three effects of increased carbon dioxide in the atmosphere. [3]

13 What are the products of incomplete combustion of ethane? [2]

14 Explain how a fossil fuel is formed. [3]

15 What is the general formula for the alkanes? [1]

Go online for the answers | Online

15 Quantitative Chemistry

Note: *For GCSE Chemistry, you will be expected to know the content of Chapter 5 for this unit.*

Percentage composition

From the formula of a compound, we can calculate the **percentage by mass** of each of the elements in the compound.

$$\% \text{ of element M in a compound} = \frac{\text{number of atoms of M in compound} \times \text{RAM of M}}{\text{RFM of compound}} \times 100$$

Example 1

Calculate the percentage composition of carbon in ethane, C_2H_6, and ethene, C_2H_4.

Name	Ethane	Ethene
Formula	C_2H_6	C_2H_4
RFM	30	28
Number of carbon atoms × RAM	24	24
%C	$\frac{24}{30} \times 100 = 80\%$	$\frac{24}{28} \times 100 = 85.71\%$

Reacting masses

Revised

From Chapter 5, you will still need to know how to carry out reacting mass calculations, converting from mass to moles, using the ratio from a balanced symbol equation to determine the number of moles of another substance in the reaction, and converting from moles to mass.

Working with solutions

Revised

Solutions are slightly more complicated because the numbers of moles depend on the **volume** of the solution (in cm^3) and on the **concentration** of the solution (in mol/dm^3). A solution that has a concentration of $1\,mol/dm^3$ has 1 mole of the solute dissolved in $1\,dm^3$ of solution. If you had $500\,cm^3$ of a solution of concentration $1\,mol/dm^3$, you would have 0.5 moles of the solute in that volume.

> **Exam tip**
>
> $1\,dm^3$ is the same as 1 litre. $1\,cm^3$ is the same as 1 ml. There are $1000\,cm^3$ in $1\,dm^3$ (1000 ml in 1 litre).

 15 Quantitative Chemistry

Solution calculations

When making a solution, a certain mass of a solid is dissolved in a certain volume of water. The **number of moles** of the solid in a solution can be calculated using:

$$\text{moles} = \frac{\text{solution volume (cm}^3\text{)} \times \text{concentration (mol/dm}^3\text{)}}{1000}$$

Example 2

1.4 g of KOH (potassium hydroxide) were dissolved completely in 100 cm^3 of water. Calculate the concentration of the solution formed in mol/dm^3.

1.4 g of solid KOH = $\dfrac{1.4}{56}$ = 0.025 moles.

0.025 moles of KOH are present in 100 cm^3.

For a solution, moles = $\dfrac{\text{solution volume (cm}^3\text{)} \times \text{concentration (mol/dm}^3\text{)}}{1000}$

$0.025 = \dfrac{100 \times \text{concentration}}{1000}$

So, concentration = $\dfrac{0.025 \times 1000}{100}$ = **0.25 mol/dm^3**.

More simply, this is 10 × the number of moles in 100 cm^3.

Determining moles of solute in a solution

The same equation is also used to calculate the number of moles of a **solute** in a certain volume of solution.

Example 3

45.0 cm^3 of a 0.1 mol/dm^3 solution of hydrochloric acid were used in a titration. Calculate the number of moles of hydrochloric acid used.

For a solution, moles = $\dfrac{\text{solution volume (cm}^3\text{)} \times \text{concentration (mol/dm}^3\text{)}}{1000}$

Moles of HCl = $\dfrac{45 \times 0.1}{1000}$ = **0.0045 moles**.

Dilution

Revised ☐

When a solution is **diluted** (by adding water) its concentration changes, but the total number of moles of solute does not. This is because water has been added but no solute has been added or removed.

The **dilution factor** is the ratio of the volume of solution to be diluted to the total volume of solution after dilution:

$$\text{dilution factor} = \frac{\text{total volume of diluted solution}}{\text{volume of original solution to be diluted}}$$

Carrying out a dilution

If 25.0 cm^3 of a solution are to be diluted to 250 cm^3, the method used is:

1 Rinse out a pipette with deionised water, and then the solution to be diluted.

2 Pipette 25.0 cm^3 of the solution into a 250 cm^3 volumetric flask.

3 Add deionised water until the bottom of the meniscus is sitting on the line in the flask.

4 Stopper the flask and shake to mix.

Example 4

25.0 cm^3 of 0.5 mol/dm^3 sodium hydroxide solution are pipetted into a volumetric flask and the volume made up to 250.0 cm^3 using deionised water – the dilution factor is 10.

$$\text{Concentration of the diluted solution} = \frac{\text{concentration of original solution}}{\text{dilution factor}}$$

The diluted solution will have a concentration of $\frac{0.5}{10} = 0.05$ mol/dm^3.

> **Exam tip**
>
> If you are calculating the concentration of the original solution from the concentration of the diluted solution, then simply multiply by the dilution factor.

Titration

Revised

A **titration** is a method of reacting two solutions together to determine the number of moles of the solute in one of the solutions.

Indicators used in titrations

Titrations involve an indicator. Two indicators are used for acid–base titrations at this level – phenolphthalein and methyl orange. A few drops of indicator are added to the solution in the conical flask, and the second solution will be added to the conical flask from a burette.

● If acid is being added to alkali, phenolphthalein changes from pink to colourless.

● If alkali is being added to acid, phenolphthalein changes from colourless to pink.

● If acid is being added to alkali, methyl orange changes from yellow to red/orange.

● If alkali is being added to acid, methyl orange changes from red to yellow/orange.

> **Exam tip**
>
> Check what solution is in the conical flask and this will give you the starting colour of the indicator.

Apparatus used in a titration

There are two main pieces of apparatus used in a titration – a **burette** and a **pipette**.

A pipette is prepared by:

● rinsing it with deionised water

● rinsing it with the solution to be used in the pipette

● using a pipette filler to draw up the solution until the bottom of the meniscus is on the line

- releasing the solution into a conical flask, touching the tip of the pipette onto the surface of the solution.

A burette is prepared by:

- rinsing it with deionised water
- rinsing it with the solution to be used in the burette
- filling the burette with the solution, ensuring the jet is filled and there are no air bubbles
- reading the volume at the bottom of the meniscus.

Method of titration

1 A measured volume (often $25.0\,cm^3$) of one solution is placed in a conical flask using a pipette and a pipette filler.

2 A few drops of indicator are added to the conical flask and the mixture swirled.

3 A burette is filled with the second solution and the volume reading taken.

4 The second solution is run out of the burette into the conical flask, while the conical flask is being swirled, until the indicator just changes colour.

5 The volume of solution added from the burette is recorded. This volume is called a **titre**.

6 The titration is carried out three times. The first value obtained is a rough value and should be ignored in calculations – it is simply a rough guide to the titre to allow faster accurate titration with dropwise addition near the end point. The second and third values are accurate and should be averaged to find the average titration volume –called the **average titre**.

Titration calculations

There are three steps to follow in basic titration calculations:

1 Enough information will be given to determine the moles of one of the solutes.

2 The balanced symbol equation between the two solutes is used to calculate the other number of moles.

3 The concentration of the other solution can be determined from the number of moles and the solution volume.

Worked example 1

25.0 cm³ of a solution of sulfuric acid of unknown concentration were placed in a conical flask using a pipette. Phenolphthalein indicator was added and the solution was titrated against $0.1\,mol/dm^3$ sodium hydroxide solution. The average titre was found to be $17.5\,cm^3$.

$$2NaOH + H_2SO_4 \rightarrow Na_2SO_4 + 2H_2O$$

a) Calculate number of moles of sodium hydroxide used in this titration. [2]

b) Calculate the number of moles of sulfuric acid that will react with this number of moles of sodium hydroxide. [1]

c) Calculate the concentration of the sulfuric acid in mol/dm^3 [2]

Answer

a) Moles of NaOH = $\dfrac{\text{solution volume (cm}^3) \times \text{concentration (mol/dm}^3)}{1000}$

$$= \frac{17.5 \times 0.1}{1000} \text{ [1]} = \mathbf{0.001\,75} \text{ [1]}$$

b) The number of moles of H_2SO_4 is half the number of moles of NaOH because in the equation 2 moles of NaOH react with 1 mole of H_2SO_4.

Moles of H_2SO_4 = $\dfrac{0.00175}{2}$ = **0.000 875** [1]

c) Concentration of H_2SO_4 = $\dfrac{\text{moles} \times 1000}{\text{solution volume (cm}^3)}$

$$= \frac{0.000875 \times 1000}{25.0} \text{ [1]} = \mathbf{0.035} \text{ [1] } \mathbf{mol/dm^3}$$

> **Exam tip**
>
> As you can see, these questions are usually structured but generally develop in three stages. First, calculate the number of moles of one substance; then determine the number of moles of the other (using the balanced symbol equation); and thirdly calculate a quantity, such as concentration, for the other substance. Sometimes the calculation gets a little more complicated but the method is the same. A dilution may be carried out on one of the solutions.

Worked example 2

A solution of ethanoic acid (CH_3COOH) is diluted by pipetting 10.0 cm^3 of the solution into a 250.0 cm^3 volumetric flask and making up the volume 250.0 cm^3 using deionised water. 25.0 cm^3 of this diluted solution were pipetted into a conical flask and titrated against 0.2 mol/dm^3 potassium hydroxide (KOH) solution using phenolphthalein indicator. 15.7 cm^3 of the potassium hydroxide solution were required for neutralisation.

$$CH_3COOH + KOH \rightarrow CH_3COOK + H_2O$$

a) Calculate the number of moles of KOH used in this titration. [2]

b) Calculate the number of moles of CH_3COOH that reacted with this number of moles of KOH. [1]

c) Calculate the concentration of the diluted CH_3COOH solution. [2]

d) Calculate the concentration of the undiluted CH_3COOH solution. [2]

Answers

a) Moles of KOH = $\dfrac{15.7 \times 0.2}{1000}$ [1] = **0.003 14** [1]

b) Moles of CH_3COOH = **0.003 14** [1] (1:1 ratio in balanced symbol equation)

c) Concentration of diluted CH_3COOH solution = $\dfrac{0.003\,14 \times 1000}{25}$ [1]
= **0.1256** [1] **mol/dm^3**

d) Concentration of undiluted CH_3COOH solution = 0.1256 × 25 [1]
= **3.14** [1] **mol/dm^3**

(the dilution factor was 25 because 10 cm^3 were diluted to 250 cm^3)

> **Exam tip**
>
> You may be asked to find the concentration of the undiluted ethanoic acid in g/dm^3 as part **e**. The RFM of CH_3COOH is 60. Concentration (g/dm^3) = concentration (mol/dm^3) × RFM
>
> Concentration (g/dm^3) = 3.14 × 60 = 188.4 g/dm^3.

Finding a formula from titration values

This type of question is usually to find the number of moles of water of crystallisation in a hydrated salt. The mole answers can be compared as before to get the simplest ratio of the salt to the water of crystallisation.

Worked example 3

A 2.86 g sample of hydrated sodium carbonate, $Na_2CO_3.xH_2O$ was dissolved in 250.0 cm³ of water. 25.0 cm³ of this solution were pipetted into a conical flask and titrated with 0.1 mol/dm³ hydrochloric acid using methyl orange indicator. The average titre was 20.0 cm³.

$$Na_2CO_3 + 2HCl \rightarrow 2NaCl + H_2O + CO_2$$

a) Calculate the number of moles of hydrochloric acid used in this titration. [2]

b) Calculate the number of moles of sodium carbonate in 25.0 cm³ of the solution. [1]

c) Calculate the number of moles of sodium carbonate present in 250.0 cm³ of the solution. [2]

d) Calculate the mass of sodium carbonate, Na_2CO_3, present in the initial sample. [2]

e) Calculate the mass of water present in the initial sample. [2]

f) Calculate the number of moles of water in the initial sample. [2]

g) Using your answers to parts **c** and **f**, determine the value of x in $Na_2CO_3.xH_2O$. [1]

Answer

a) Moles of HCl $= \dfrac{20 \times 0.1}{1000}$ [1] $= \mathbf{0.002}$ [1]

b) Moles of Na_2CO_3 in 25.0 cm³ = **0.001** [1] (0.002 ÷ 2 because of the ratio in the equation)

c) Moles of Na_2CO_3 in 250.0 cm³ = 0.001 × 10 [1] = **0.01** [1]

d) Mass of Na_2CO_3 in 250.0 cm³ = 0.01 × 106 [1] = **1.06** [1] **g**

e) Mass of water = 2.86 − 1.06 = **1.8** [1] **g**

f) Moles of water $= \dfrac{1.8}{18} = \mathbf{0.1}$ [1]

g) Moles of Na_2CO_3 = 0.01; moles of water = **0.1**

Simplest ratio $Na_2CO_3 : H_2O$ = 1 : 10, so $\boldsymbol{x = 10}$ [1]

A titration may also be used to determine the identity of an unknown metal in a compound.

Worked example 4

2.8 g of an unknown metal hydroxide, MOH, were dissolved in deionised water and transferred to a volumetric flask. The volume was made up to 250.0 cm³ using deionised water. 25.0 cm³ of this solution were titrated against 0.25 mol/dm³ hydrochloric acid using phenolphthalein indicator. The table on page 148 gives the results of this titration.

	Initial burette volume /cm³	Final burette volume /cm³	Titre /cm³
Rough	0.0	20.8	20.8
Accurate 1	20.8	40.8	20.0
Accurate 2	0.0	20.0	20.0

a) Calculate the average titre. [2]

b) State the colour change of the indicator at the end point. [2]

c) Calculate the number of moles of hydrochloric acid used. [2]

The equation for the reaction can be written:

$MOH + HCl \rightarrow MCl + H_2O$

d) Calculate the number of moles of MOH present in 25.0 cm³. [1]

e) Calculate the number of moles of MOH present in 250.0 cm³. [2]

f) Using the initial mass of MOH used and your answer to part **e** calculate the RFM of MOH and the RAM of M. [2]

g) Using your *Data Leaflet*, determine the identity of M. [1]

Exam tip
The table of titration results given in this question is a common way of representing this data. You should remember *not* to use the rough result when calculating the average titre. Always include the units of solution volume (cm³).

Exam tip
1 mark is awarded if you get the colour change the wrong way round, so always make an attempt at an answer.

Exam tip
Remember to look at the relative atomic mass on the Periodic Table in the *Data Leaflet* and *not* the atomic number. Yttrium (atomic number 39) would be a common incorrect answer to this question.

Answers

a) **20.0 cm³** [2]

Note: *1 mark is awarded if the rough value is included in the calculation.*

b) **Pink** [1] to **colourless** [1]

c) Moles of HCl = $\dfrac{20 \times 0.25}{1000}$ [1] = **0.005** [1]

d) Moles of MOH in 25.0 cm³ = **0.005** [1] (due to 1 : 1 ratio in equation)

e) Moles of MOH in 250.0 cm³ = 0.005 × 10 [1] = **0.05** [1]

f) RFM of MOH = $\dfrac{2.8}{0.05}$ = 56 [1] so RAM of M = 56 − 16 − 1 = **39** [1]

g) Identity of M is **potassium/K** [1]

Revision Questions

Tested ☐

1 Calculate the percentage of carbon present in butane, C_4H_{10} [2]

2 Which of the following chlorides contains the highest percentage of chlorine:

CCl_4, HCl or PCl_5? [2]

3 Explain how you would prepare a burette for use in a titration. [3]

4 State what colour change you would expect to see if an acid was added to an alkali containing methyl orange indicator. [2]

5 A 0.6 g sample of magnesium was reacted with 2.0 mol/dm³ sulfuric acid:

$Mg + H_2SO_4 \rightarrow MgSO_4 + H_2$

Calculate the volume of 2.0 mol/dm³ sulfuric acid required to react with this mass of magnesium. [4]

6 Calculate the mass of aluminium oxide which could be formed by burning 2 g of powdered aluminium in air:

$4Al + 3O_2 \rightarrow 2Al_2O_3$ [5]

7 Explain how you would prepare a pipette for use in a titration. [4]

8 25.0 cm³ of a solution of potassium hydroxide were pipetted into a conical flask along with a few drops of phenolphthalein indicator. A burette was filled with 0.25 mol/dm³ sulfuric acid and titration carried out. The average titration figure was 19.5 cm³. The equation for the reaction is:

$2KOH + H_2SO_4 \rightarrow K_2SO_4 + 2H_2O$

a) Calculate the number of moles of sulfuric acid used. [2]

b) Calculate the number of moles of potassium hydroxide in 25.0 cm³ of solution. [1]

c) Calculate the concentration of the potassium hydroxide solution. [2]

9 A sample of 0.56 g of an unknown metal hydroxide, MOH, was dissolved in 100.0 cm³ of water. 25.0 cm³ of the solution were titrated with 0.2 mol/dm³ hydrochloric acid using a suitable indicator. The volume of acid required for complete neutralisation was found to be 17.5 cm³. The equation for the reaction can be represented as:

$MOH + HCl \rightarrow MCl + H_2O$

a) Calculate the number of moles of hydrochloric acid used. [2]

b) Calculate the number of moles of MOH in 25.0 cm³ of the solution. [1]

c) Calculate number of moles of MOH in 100.0 cm³ of the solution. [2]

d) Using the mass of MOH and the number of moles, calculate the RFM of the metal hydroxide, MOH. [2]

e) Calculate the RAM of M. [2]

f) Using your *Data Leaflet*, determine the identity of M. [1]

10 10.0 cm³ of a solution of potassium hydroxide were diluted to 250.0 cm³ in a volumetric flask. A 25.0 cm³ sample of this solution was titrated against 0.05 mol/dm³ hydrochloric acid and the average titre was found to be 20.7 cm³:

$KOH + HCl \rightarrow KCl + H_2O$

a) Calculate the number of moles of hydrochloric acid used in this titration. [2]

b) Calculate the number of moles of potassium hydroxide present in 25.0 cm³ of the solution in the conical flask. [1]

c) Calculate the concentration of the diluted potassium hydroxide solution in mol/dm³ [2]

d) Calculate the dilution factor used and use it to calculate the concentration of the original solution of potassium hydroxide in mol/dm³ [2]

e) Calculate the concentration of the original solution of potassium hydroxide in g/dm³. [2]

Go online for the answers Online

16 Materials

Raw materials

Revised

The five major sources of raw materials with examples are shown in the table below.

Sources of raw materials

Source	Examples of materials
Earth	Lime (from limestone), salt (from rock salt), aluminium (from bauxite), iron (from haematite)
Sea	Water, sodium chloride (salt)
Air	Oxygen, nitrogen, argon and other noble gases
Crude oil	Plastics, petrol, diesel, bitumen
Living things	Cotton, wool, wood, rubber

Natural and synthetic materials

Revised

Natural materials are those derived directly from raw materials. **Synthetic** materials are also called **man-made** materials. Raw materials are put through a manufacturing process to make a synthetic material. Here are some examples of natural and synthetic materials:

● natural materials – cotton, wool, silk, wood, rubber, gold

● synthetic materials – polythene, PVC, glass, iron, aluminium.

Nanotechnology

Revised

A nanometre (nm) is a unit of length – it is 10^{-9} m. 1 million nanometres make up a millimetre (1 mm = 1 000 000 nm) or 1000 million nanometres make up 1 metre (10^9 nm = 1 m).

Nanoscience, or **nanotechnology**, uses particles with sizes in the range 1–100 nm. For comparison, a human hair is 80 000 nm wide. At this size, the particles have a very large surface area, which gives them different properties to traditional materials.

● The most recent sun protection creams use **nanoparticles**. Older suncreams used zinc oxide, which leaves a white residue on the skin. The new nanoparticle suncreams rub on as a clear film.

● Nanoparticles of silver nitrate are used in wound dressings in hospitals. Silver nanoparticles kill bacteria, which prevents the wound from becoming infected. Silver nanoparticles are also used in soaps to kill bacteria on washing and in socks where they kill odour-causing bacteria.

● Carbon nanotubes are 100 times stronger than steel but 6 times lighter and can be used to strengthen any material. A carbon nanotube is a single layer of graphite rolled into a tube.

- More recently, graphene (a single layer taken from graphite) has been shown to be 200 times stronger than steel – it also conducts electricity, making it very useful in the electronics industry.

Risks linked with these materials relate to their unknown effects in the environment – for example, silver nanoparticles can be absorbed through the skin and cause discoloration of it. There is a fear that nanoparticles may also be able to penetrate further into the body interfering with many processes. Breathing-in nanoparticles may cause inflammation of the lungs and the particles may be absorbed into the bloodstream. Most of the risk centres around the unknown and more research is needed.

Extraction of metals from their ores

Revised ☐

Most metal ores are oxides of the metal – some are converted to oxides of the metal before the metal is extracted.

- The lowest reactivity metals are found uncombined in nature (also called native).
- Metals that are high in the reactivity series are extracted by **electrolysis**.
- Metals that are low in the reactivity series are extracted by **reduction** with carbon or carbon monoxide.
- For metals such as aluminium and those above it in the reactivity series, **electrolysis** must be used to extract the metal from its ore.
- All methods of extracting a metal from its ore require reduction, which can be explained either in terms of a gain of electrons or a loss of oxygen (page 100).

Reaction of carbon with metal oxides

Carbon is a non-metal but it can be included in the reactivity series of the metals because it can displace some metals from their compounds.

      increasing reactivity

$$\text{Cu} \quad \text{Fe} \quad \text{Zn} \quad \text{Al} \quad \text{Mg} \quad \text{Ca} \quad \text{Na} \quad \text{K} \quad \longrightarrow$$
$$\qquad\qquad\quad\uparrow$$
$$\qquad\qquad\quad\text{C}$$

Carbon is used to extract metals below aluminium in the reactivity series.

Electrolysis

Revised ☐

Note: *This section on the principles of electrolysis is C1 in Double Award Chemistry.*

Two graphite rods, placed in a liquid and connected externally to a power supply such as a battery or a power pack, can be used to test if a liquid conducts electricity.

If a liquid conducts electricity and is **decomposed** by it, then **electrolysis** is taking place.

● Electrolysis is the decomposition of a liquid electrolyte using a direct current of electricity.

● The **electrolyte** is the liquid or solution that conducts electricity and is decomposed by it.

● The graphite rods used are called **electrodes**.

● Graphite is used because it is a good conductor of electricity and is unreactive.

● The negative electrode is called the **cathode**.

● The positive electrode is called the **anode**.

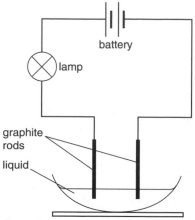

↑ Testing to see if a liquid conducts electricity

How electrolysis works

All electrolytes conduct electricity because they have **free ions** that can move and carry charge. When positive and negative ions are free to move, the positive ions (called cations) move to the negative electrode (called the cathode), and the negative ions (called anions) move to the positive electrode (called the anode).

● The positive ions at the negative electrode (cathode) gain electrons to become atoms.

● The gain of electrons is called reduction – reduction happens at the cathode.

● The negative ions at the positive electrode (anode) lose electrons to become atoms, which may combine to form diatomic molecules for elements such as chlorine, Cl_2, and bromine, Br_2.

● The loss of electrons is called oxidation – oxidation happens at the anode.

● Molten ionic compound and aqueous ionic compounds are the most common electrolytes.

Typical apparatus used to electrolyse a molten electrolyte is shown in the diagram below.

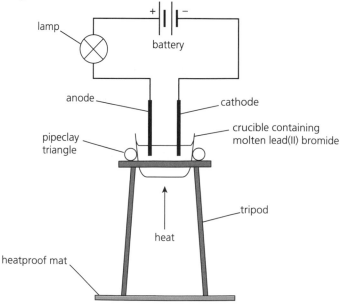

↑ **Apparatus used to electrolyse a molten electrolyte**

Observations and half-equations

Note: *Half-equations are Higher tier content.*

For each of the following electrolytes, you must be able to describe what is observed at both electrodes. You must also be able to write **half-equations** to represent the reactions at each of the electrodes in terms of loss or gain of electrons.

- First, identify the positive metal ions and the negative non-metal ions present in the ionic compound.
- The metal ions in the molten compound are attracted to the cathode, where the ions gain electrons to form atoms.
- The non-metal ions in the molten compound are attracted to the anode, where the ions lose electrons to forms atoms. For diatomic elements, two atoms combine together to form a molecule.
- It is often easier to write the half-equations first, and then work out what would be observed from the products of the electrolysis.

Example 1: Molten lead(II) bromide, $PbBr_2$

Cathode: positive ion: Pb^{2+}

Half-equation: $Pb^{2+} + 2e^- \rightarrow Pb$

Observations: Silvery, grey liquid formed, which sinks to the bottom (can only be seen when the molten electrolyte is poured off).

Anode: negative ion: Br^-

Half-equation: $2Br^- \rightarrow Br_2 + 2e^-$

Observations: red-brown pungent gas evolved.

Example 2: Molten lithium chloride, LiCl

Cathode: positive ion: Li^+

Half-equation: $Li^+ + e^- \rightarrow Li$

Observations: Silvery, grey liquid formed.

Anode: negative ion: Cl^-

Half-equation: $2Cl^- \rightarrow Cl_2 + 2e^-$

Observations: yellow-green, pungent gas evolved.

Example 3: Molten sodium iodide, NaI

This is an example of applying your knowledge to an unfamiliar metal halide.

Cathode: positive ion: Na^+

Half-equation: $Na^+ + e^- \rightarrow Na$

Observations: Silvery, grey liquid formed.

Anode: negative ion: I^-

Half-equation: $2I^- \rightarrow I_2 + 2e^-$

Observations: Purple, pungent gas evolved.

> **Exam tip**
>
> Because these are all molten ionic compounds, heat is being applied and so a low melting point and low density metal such as lithium, sodium or potassium will appear as a grey liquid around the cathode. Lead has a relatively low melting point compared to the transition metals, but is dense and so will sink to the bottom.
>
> The halogens will all appear as gases if they are produced at the anode during molten electrolysis.
>
> If a molten metal oxide is electrolysed, oxygen gas is produced at the anode and the observations would include a colourless, odourless gas being evolved (though often this can be difficult to see apart from a few bubbles around the electrode).

Extraction of aluminium from its ore

Aluminium metal is extracted from its ore using electrolysis – aluminium ore is called **bauxite**.

● Bauxite is purified to form aluminium oxide (called alumina). The alumina is dissolved in molten cryolite to reduce its melting point and increase its conductivity.

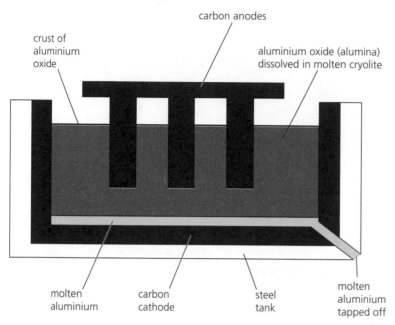

↑ **Apparatus used to extract aluminium from its ore**

● A crust of aluminium oxide keeps heat in. The operating temperature is 900 °C.

● The cathode and anode are both made of carbon.

● The reaction at the cathode is: $Al^{3+} + 3e^- \rightarrow Al$

● The reaction at the anode is: $2O^{2-} \rightarrow O_2 + 4e^-$

● The carbon anode has to be replaced periodically because it wears away as it reacts with oxygen: $C + O_2 \rightarrow CO_2$

● The reaction at the cathode is reduction because aluminium ions are gaining electrons, and the gain of electrons is reduction.

● The reaction at the anode is oxidation because oxide ions are losing electrons, and the loss of electrons is oxidation.

● The extraction of aluminium is expensive because the cost of electricity is high and a high temperature is needed to keep the aluminium oxide molten. The use of cryolite increases the conductivity and reduces the operating temperature, saving money. The aluminium oxide crust keeps some heat in, again saving money.

● The expense of recycling aluminium is only a fraction of the cost of producing new aluminium from bauxite. This is why it is important to recycle materials such as aluminium – it saves resources, saves energy, prevents waste going to landfill and costs less.

Exam tip

When explaining oxidation at the anode or reduction at the cathode during electrolysis, always include the names of the ions gaining or losing electrons and then state the definition of either oxidation or reduction.

Factors affecting the siting of an aluminium extraction plant

A company will make a decision to site an aluminium extraction site in a particular area based on a number of criteria:

● local sources for some of the raw materials

● good sea, rail and road transport links for delivery of materials, transport of the workforce and transport of waste away from the site

● a deep-water port for deliveries of raw materials from overseas

● a good electricity supply, especially a renewable one such as hydroelectric power

● a reasonable size of local population with available skilled workforce

● not close to any conservation areas or areas of outstanding natural beauty.

Extraction of iron in the blast furnace
Revised

A simplified diagram of the blast furnace is shown below.

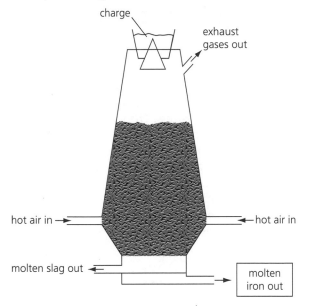

↑ **A blast furnace**

The solid material put into the blast furnace is called the **charge**. It is made up of **iron ore** (**haematite**, Fe_2O_3), **limestone** (**calcium carbonate**, $CaCO_3$) and **coke** (**carbon**, C). Hot air is blasted in through pipes near the bottom of the blast furnace. Reduction of iron ore happens because the oxygen is removed from the iron(III) oxide *or* Fe^{3+} ions gain electrons to form Fe atoms.

There are five reactions involved in this process. The production of the reducing agent (carbon monoxide) occurs in two of them. The reduction of iron ore occurs in one reaction and finally the removal of the acidic impurities occurs in two reactions.

Production of the reducing agent

1 Coke burns in oxygen (from hot air) to produce carbon dioxide:

$$C + O_2 \rightarrow CO_2$$

2 Carbon dioxide reacts with more coke (carbon) to produce the reducing agent, which is carbon monoxide:

$$CO_2 + C \rightarrow 2CO$$

Reduction of iron ore to iron

3 Iron(III) oxide reacts with carbon monoxide to produce molten iron and carbon dioxide:

$$Fe_2O_3 + 3CO \rightarrow 2Fe + 3CO_2$$

Note: *This is the oxidation and reduction stage of the extraction of iron. Carbon (and carbon monoxide) will reduce iron(III) oxide to iron. Remember that the iron(III) oxide loses oxygen and loss of oxygen is reduction. The carbon monoxide is oxidised because it gains oxygen and gain of oxygen is oxidation. For the iron, it may also be stated that iron(III) ions (Fe^{3+}) gain electrons ($Fe^{3+} + 3e^- \rightarrow Fe$) and gain of electrons is reduction.*

Removal of acidic impurities

4 Calcium carbonate thermally decomposes to form calcium oxide and carbon dioxide:

$$CaCO_3 \rightarrow CaO + CO_2$$

5 Silicon dioxide impurities react with calcium oxide to form molten slag (calcium silicate, $CaSiO_3$):

$$SiO_2 + CaO \rightarrow CaSiO_3$$

The molten slag and molten iron fall to the bottom of the furnace. Iron is denser than slag, so it sinks below the slag. They are tapped off separately at the base of the blast furnace.

> **Exam tip**
>
> Many questions about iron involve the materials added to the blast furnace, the materials removed from it and the equations for the five reactions that occur during the process. The most common mistakes are to forget to write 'molten slag' and 'molten iron' and to get the order in which they are removed mixed up – remember that molten iron is denser than molten slag.

Socio-economic, environmental and ethical concerns

Revised

The use of materials is widespread and their production, disposal and recycling generates debate. The table on page 157 gives details of some of the positive and negative points used in the evaluation of recycling materials containing aluminium, iron and plastics, such as polythene and PVC, as opposed to their disposal or the production of new materials.

It can be viewed as our duty to recycle materials as there are so many advantages in terms of the environment.

Recycling compared to disposal of materials

Recycling	Disadvantages	• sorting recycled materials is labour intensive and expensive
	Advantages	• less mining/drilling for raw materials • less use of energy • less pollution caused by dust/increased traffic/noise pollution • less destruction of natural habitats/less subsidence caused by mining • fewer eyesores created • saves resources
Disposal by incineration or landfill	Disadvantages	• toxic/harmful gases released into the atmosphere • landfill wastes land • ash residue from incineration is toxic and specialised landfill is needed • incineration of waste prevents landfill • more transport of waste to incineration sites, as opposed to local landfill sites
	Advantages	• heat energy from incineration can be harnessed to generate electricity
Production of new materials	Disadvantages	• more mining/drilling for raw materials • more raw materials used • more energy used in the production of the new materials • more pollution caused by dust/increased traffic/noise • more destruction of natural habitats/more subsidence caused by mining • more eyesores created
	Advantages	• workforce skilled in industrial processing

Revision Questions

Tested

1 Name three synthetic materials. [3]

2 State two objections that residents in a small village might have to the siting of an aluminium extraction site in the countryside near the village. [2]

3 State the raw materials used in the extraction of iron from its ore. [4]

4 What is observed at the anode during the electrolysis of molten lead(II) bromide? [3]

5 Write a half-equation for the reaction at the anode during the electrolysis of molten lithium chloride. [3]

6 What is meant by the term 'electrolysis'? [2]

7 What material is used for the electrodes during the extraction of aluminium? [1]

8 What is: **a)** an anode; **b)** a cathode? [2]

9 What does the term 'electrolyte' mean? [3]

10 State **two** reasons why graphite is used for the electrodes during the electrolysis of molten lead(II) bromide. [2]

11 What is the name of aluminium ore, and what material is the purified ore dissolved in before electrolysis? [1]

12 Write a balanced symbol equation for the reduction of iron(III) oxide in the blast furnace using carbon monoxide. [3]

13 Explain why the anode has to be replaced during the electrolytic extraction of aluminium. You may use an equation to help answer this question. [2]

14 Write a half-equation for the discharge of aluminium ions at the cathode. [3]

15 Suggest **two** reasons why it is better to recycle materials than to send them to landfill or incineration. [2]

Go online for the answers

Online

Index